TRADE AND COLLECT COLLECTABLES

(Revised edition 2012)

Published by Hartley Publications Ltd.
PO Box 100, Devizes, Wiltshire, SN10 4TE

Typeset, make-up and printing by
Wentrow Media, 49 Lancaster Road, Bowerhill Trading Estate, Melksham, Wiltshire, SN12 6SS.

CONTENTS

INTRODUCTION

Welcome to Trade And Collect Collectables (revised edition 2012), brought to you by Collecticus.

First of all, it will be helpful if you understand what COLLECTICUS is all about.

Since it all began in 2004, collectable items are sourced, photographed and then published in the Collecticus monthly magazine. At the same time, each item is added to the Collecticus postal and internet auction. Readers of the magazine then bid on the featured items.

The purpose of Collecticus is not to make a profit from the sale of the collectable items, but to analyse sales performance. In other words, by offering particular items for sale it is possible to establish current market trends.

The auction results become the most important element of Collecticus and build into a comprehensive price guide.

This book is a compilation of some of the hundreds of fascinating collectables that have passed through Collecticus, plus a range of articles on various collecting subjects and a detailed glossary.

Make sure you check out the Collecticus website; there's plenty of information for anyone interested in the world of collectables.

www.collecticus.co.uk

INVESTING IN COLLECTABLE ITEMS

Many collectors collect for fun – there is a subject they are interested in, and they collect relating to that subject. However, there are many other collectors who look on collecting as a business. As with any business, buying low and selling high is the name of the game; and it is important to acquire stock that has a strong chance of selling for profit.

While there is no guarantee that a particular collectable item represents an investment potential, there is little doubt that many items do. The following guidelines should assist in procuring good quality items.

- Look for items that are not likely to have been deemed collectable in the first place, or items that are rare and unusual. Scarcity drives up the value, so uncommon items will often (although not always) represent a better investment.

- Concentrate on items that are small. Not only does this make items easier to store, but it also makes them easier to post should you decide to sell them to someone who isn't able to collect the item in person.

- Look for unusual items in current day-to-day use NOW and store them away safely.

- Concentrate on a particular subject. If you focus your collecting, it will stop your collection from becoming too large and you will start to become an expert. If you know a lot about your subject, then you will know the best times to sell, the best places to sell, and the right prices to be asking for.

- While you may build your collection on the basis that an item of any condition will do, it is recommended you collect only the best quality possible to improve investment potential.

- Log every item in your collection and take photographs. This will function as a stock list as well as being useful for insurance purposes. Make sure you store the stock list and photographs in a different location to where you store the actual items.

- Do your homework. Do not buy items without establishing if you are buying at a good price. Also, make sure you know how to recognise fake and reproduction items.

STORING COLLECTABLE ITEMS

- Always package your items individually, with a note specifying the date the item was purchased and how much you paid. Notes on the item's history may also prove useful.

- For paper items, include a backing board, slightly larger than the item itself. Do NOT fold the items.

- Flat items, such as vinyl records, should be stored upright to avoid bowing.

- Never store items in a place where there may be vermin. For safety's sake, your items should be stored inside containers.

- Avoid using sticky tape to seal plastic bags, as there is a risk the tape may get stuck to an item and ruin it. Try to use bags with a plastic interlocking seal strip instead.

- Do not wrap silver items in newspapers or put rubber bands around items such as spoons. This leaves marks that are difficult to remove.

- Never wrap decks of cards or postcards with rubber bands, as this can irreparably damage the cardstock.

- Rare books should be stored rather than read. Opening the pages of old books can cause damage.

- Do not stack boxes on top of other boxes unless absolutely necessary. If you have to stack some boxes, make sure you stack bigger boxes ON TOP OF smaller boxes, as this will prevent the weight of the smaller boxes causing the lids of bigger boxes to be crushed or bowed.

- Store all items in a cool dark place. A loft may experience extremes of temperature so may not be ideal.

- Do not clean old items before storing them, unless you are sure that cleaning the items will not cause any harm.

BUYING **AT CAR BOOT SALES**

- Arrive early to catch the real treasures.

- Take a rucksack to carry what you buy.

- Make sure you have plenty of small change.

- Take a supply of plastic bags and some A4 plastic or card wallets for protecting your purchases.

- Watch out for pickpockets.

- The first stall you visit should be the latest one to set up.

- Dress like a pauper, so it's easier to haggle.

- Be careful when buying electrical items, they may not be safe to use. They may not work at all.

- ALWAYS HAGGLE.

- Be prepared to get down on your hands and knees to sift through boxes of oddments. Some great little treasures can be found at the bottom of a box of "junk."

- Never show excitement. A deadpan expression is required with every offer.

- Don't take your dog. Many boot sales now ban them.

- If it is a hot day, remember to take some sun cream. Conversely, if it is a cold day, wrap up warm.

- Take your own food and a flask of coffee, so you don't have to waste time queuing at the refreshment stands.

- Don't push and shove when looking at a stall. Boot sales are supposed to be friendly affairs.

- Tender the exact sum negotiated.

- Don't try to outbid someone else on an item he or she has already picked up. It's commonly accepted that once you hold an item in your hand, it's your first option.

- Don't be aggressive when you haggle.

- Don't tell a seller that his or her items are rubbish.

- Don't interfere with someone else's sale. Let the buyer and seller negotiate the arrangement themselves.

SELLING AT CAR BOOT SALES

- Don't take items that can be easily damaged.

- Be positive. If asked for a "best price," don't respond in a quizzical tone of voice, as if to say "Is that all right?"

- Do not put items aside for potential purchasers for any reason, unless you take a non-refundable deposit first.

- Take plenty of empty plastic bags and newspaper to wrap items.

- Don't keep your money anywhere that requires you to turn your back on your stall.

- Placing an item in a clear plastic wallet can give it a feeling of being valuable, and allows you to attach a price sticker without causing damage.

- Try placing price tags underneath items, forcing potential buyers to pick up the items and turn them over. This gives you a clear indication of their interest. (Please note: this suggestion is not recommended for breakable items.)

- If the weather looks like it will be unpredictable, take a gazebo with you. These can be purchased quite cheaply from household stores, and can be a real lifesaver if you get caught in a downpour.

- When using a fold-up table, cover it with a white or cream sheet. This will help bring out the colour in your sale items, and will generally make the stall look more attractive. Your items may look even more valuable.

WHAT IS IT WORTH?

A typical example of an item that can be found at a Collectors' Fair is a 1960 Butlin's (Skegness) badge, and many people will be aware of the value of such an item (approximately £5 - £7). Hence, when you offer a mere £2, the seller will politely advise you of the situation.

What the seller really needs to do is bring hundreds of Butlin's badge collectors together and auction his badge. If he can do this, he is likely to achieve a top market value. However, to bring enough people together can be costly, and this (hidden) cost eventually has to be passed on to the buyer.

If you remove this costly element of finding the right buyer (for example, selling the badge among many other items on a car boot stall) the actual cost of the sale becomes much less and therefore the selling price should be below the expected top retail value.

Many sellers quote "book price" to justify a high price, but car boot sales are not the ideal place to sell a specialised item, if top retail value is sought.

Now, once you have politely explained the theory to the seller, you can proceed to buy at below the "true value" and, once you have acquired the item, set about your task of making a profit in a wider marketplace.

SOCIAL HISTORY

A tiny scrap of paper, often perceived as rubbish, can actually have meaning and significance in terms of social history. An example would be an old sweet wrapper.

It is not desirable to keep all sweet wrappers or every scrap of paper, but selective saving (particularly of items in excellent condition) can result in collectable items for the future.

In the example of a sweet wrapper, this becomes so much more desirable when the product has long ceased production; even more so if the manufacturer has ceased trading completely.

Did the manufacturer employ large numbers of people? Did the area rely heavily on that company for livelihoods and social activities? Some people may have devoted their entire lives to that one company. Summer holidays may even have been influenced by the company, with social club visits to the seaside, etc.

Social history is generally fascinating, and collectors are helping to preserve it for generations to come. Car boot sales are playing a role, although many people are totally unaware.

On a more financial note, documenting the historical background of a collectable item will nearly always add value to it.

PROVENANCE

Provenance concerns evidence of the origin and history of ownership of a particular item.

Provenance can be proved in all manner of ways, from scientific methods to something as simple as a shop receipt or deed of ownership, and may considerably increase the value of your treasures. For example, a library stamp in a book could link the book to a person or place of historical importance, causing the investment potential of the book to increase.

Many autographs (especially those purchased from internet auctions and stores) will be sold with a Certificate Of Authenticity (COA). It is important to note that such certificates are often worthless in proving the authenticity of an autograph. Any provenance can be faked, and the collector should be wary of this. The more evidence of provenance there is, the more likely the item is to be genuine, and the more interesting the item will be.

Proving provenance is not always easy, but you should be conscious of it. For example, if you get the chance to acquire a famous person's autograph:

1. Take a photograph of the autograph being written, using a camera that has a time and date stamp.

2. Get the autograph on something dated (like a concert programme).

This not only helps to prove the autograph is genuine, but gives the autograph a place in history.

THE GUIDE TO COLLECTABLES (PAGES 16 - 179)

Collecticus is a monthly magazine featuring all manner of collectable items. Every item featured in the magazine subsequently goes up for sale at auction. Subscribers can bid on the items by post or by using the Collecticus website, and because items are listed with low start prices and no reserves, the final hammer prices give a good indication of current market trends.

On the following pages (16 - 179), we have featured a wide range of items that were sold through the Collecticus auction.

For each item we have included a brief description, a year of manufacture or issue, the condition (see below), the date when sold, and the price the item realised in the auction.

Dates in brackets are estimated.

Letters in brackets indicate the condition of the item:

Poor   (p)
Fair   (f)
Good   (g)
Very Good   (vg)
Excellent   (ex)
Mint   (mnt)

Conditions may be combined to give a more accurate description. For example, an item in poor to fair condition would be listed as (p-f).

AA (AUTOMOBILE ASSOCIATION)

The Automobile Association (AA) was formed in 1905 by a group of motoring enthusiasts meeting at the Trocadero restaurant in London's West End. The Association was originally created with the intention of helping motorists to avoid police speed traps, but eventually it worked towards creating safer roads by erecting some of the first danger and warning signs. Subsequent activities included route planning and roadside assistance.

There is a great deal of AA memorabilia available for collectors, ranging from roadside phone boxes and motorcycle sidecars all the way down to simple route maps and membership certificates. The huge array of collectables can be quite daunting to begin with, and sadly a fair amount of what you will find at car boot sales is of little or no real monetary value.

▲ AA telephone box emblem sign. (1935). 406 x 333mm. (g). Sold November 2009: £100

There is a great deal of ephemera relating to the AA, most of which is of interest to collectors yet worth relatively little (for example, AA Drive magazines and guidebooks are only really worth acquiring in bulk at a discount price). AA route maps can be fun to collect, but are similarly unlikely to sell for a fortune; however, early examples of personalised route plans do have a higher value. The AA first offered the service of providing route plans for members in 1910, and to begin with such plans were prepared by hand. By the late 1920s so many routes were being produced that the value drops considerably, and it is unlikely that a prepared route from this period will realise more than £1 at auction (although, as always, there will be exceptions).

Perhaps the most interesting items under the heading of AA ephemera are the AA handbooks, the first of which was produced in 1908. Unfortunately, there is only one known copy of the 1908 handbook in existence today, and it is very unlikely that any more will suddenly turn up at a collectors' fair. Note that the 1909 edition of the handbook is exactly the same as the 1908 edition (except for the date), so buy with care.

From 1908 to 1915, and then again from 1919 to 1930, the handbook was produced annually. Handbooks from this period are obviously the most desirable but are also the hardest to find, particularly in reasonable condition. Most of the handbooks that are readily available at boot sales and internet websites will date from around the 1950s to the 1970s; because of the age, many people mistakenly believe these handbooks to be worth large sums, but unfortunately most of the handbooks from the early 1950s are only worth £5 or so, even in very good condition, and handbooks from the 1970s will rarely sell for more than £1.

▲ AA Members Handbook. 1961. (g). Sold November 2010: £1.10

Also, there seems to be little demand for membership cards and certificates, and you will often see these failing to sell on website auctions. This could possibly be a collecting subject that will gain popularity in the future, and it could be possible to build a good collection right now at very little expense.

▲ AA advertising leaflet. 1964. (g). Sold April 2010: £5.10

In 1911, the AA started to install telephone boxes on certain roads, and cabinets containing towels and brushes at hotels; by 1919 members were being issued keys to these boxes. The keys are incredibly easy to buy, sell, and trade thanks to their small size and light weight, but they are not worth huge sums. Any key issued prior to 1947 had a round head, and these offer the best investment potential. Anything dated from 1947 onwards (made by Yale) is likely to sell for little more than £1.

(A) The first key (1912 – 1919) is now hard to find and has a minimum value of £35 (in good condition). It has a fretted crossed 'AA' in the head.

(B) The next key was a size larger than its predecessor. It was made by H & T Vaughan of Willenhall and was only issued in 1920. It is not readily available, so it is one to watch out for. Expect a minimum value of £15 (in good condition).

(C) This is another key that was only produced for one year (1921). It is smaller than previous examples. Like the 1920 key, this one carried the date, but it was also stamped with the words "The Key to the Open Road." It is interesting to note that the year was never included again on any of the keys. Expect to pay £20 for an example in good condition.

(D) From 1922 – 1946 the rounded head shape continued (minus the year). The "Open Road" line was replaced with the message "Property of the Automobile Association." This key is still fairly hard to find but cannot be classed as rare, so the value of this one drops dramatically to £8 in good condition and a little more for examples in better condition.

(E) In 1947 the design was changed and stamped by the maker Yale (who had taken over the business of H & T Vaughan). This lasted until 1966. Many were produced so they are reasonably easy to find and, in good condition or better, can sell for £3.

(F) The final key was issued in 1967, coinciding with the change of logo. Supply was plentiful so the value is half its predecessor, although this type will quite often fetch more if the condition is very good or better.

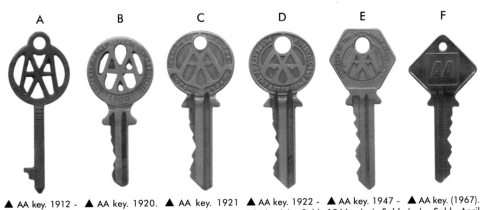

A	B	C	D	E	F
▲ AA key. 1912 – 1919. (g-vg). Sold March 2011: £35	▲ AA key. 1920. (f -g). Sold March 2011: £15	▲ AA key. 1921 Sold March 2011: £20	▲ AA key. 1922 - 1946. (g). Sold March 2011: £8	▲ AA key. 1947 - 1966. (vg). Sold April 2011: £8.10	▲ AA key. (1967). (ex). Sold April 2010: £1.60

The humble grille badge is one of the most popular pieces of AA memorabilia, but it is necessary to purchase badges with great care to improve the chance of selling for profit and even a small amount of knowledge will be a significant advantage.

Such badges were first introduced in 1906, nine months after the AA had been formed. Any badges from this very early period are worthy of attention, in particular the two thousand motorcycle badges that were issued in 1907 (the first of which was numbered 10001). Any badge issued prior to the 1945 redesign, especially a badge with all of the original fastenings, should prove a solid investment; but be prepared to pay about £40 for a good condition example from the 1920s.

▲ AA grille badge. (g). Sold January 2009: £14.70

▲ AA grille badge. (1970). (g). Sold September 2008: £5.00

Square badges were introduced in February 1967 and are rather easy to find; as such, an example in excellent condition is generally expected to sell for around £4. However, in the right market, badges dating from this period have been known to sell for upwards of £10. Interesting modern variants such as the yellow on black Maltese badge are also worthy of note.

The numbers appearing on AA badges were issue numbers. They give a good indication of when a badge was produced:

- 1 to 999,999 - 1906-30
- A-P suffixes - 1930-45
- RST suffixes - 1946-56
  (Flat motorcycle badges)
- WXYZA suffixes - 1956-67
  (Domed motorcycle badges)
- OA to OZ prefixes - 1945-57
- 1A-9A prefix - 1957-59
- 1B-9B prefix - 1960-61
- 1C-9C prefix - 1962-63
- 1D-9D prefix - 1964-65
- 1E-9E prefix - 1966-67

After 1967, the badge became square and there was no longer any number on it.

ACTION MAN

Palitoy's Action Man figures were introduced on the UK market in 1966. They were inspired by the Hasbro Toy Company's GI Joe figures, which had proved to be a big hit in America.

The Action Man toys were produced to a very high standard of quality, and it was possible to buy a huge variety of very realistic outfits and equipment, so it is hardly surprising that the toys have now become incredibly popular with collectors. Of course, being toys, the Action Man figures were designed to be played with, often going through more wars than their real-life counterparts; and it is not easy to find examples in good condition.

The first three figures produced were a soldier, sailor, and pilot, all with painted hair and eyes. After four years, a flocking process was developed that would allow the toys to have realistic hair and beards.

By 1973, Action Man had gripping hands. Moving "eagle-eyes" were used from 1976, and in 1981 a sharpshooter head was introduced. This head was designed to pivot back further than the previous heads, and an ingenious Adam's apple on the figure's neck stopped the head dropping forwards again.

Palitoys attempted to keep up with changing trends, and the popularity of phenomenon like Star Wars, by releasing space figures, aliens, and gigantic monsters, but by 1984 production was ceased, and Action Man was replaced with a smaller action toy called Action Force.

Action Man got a makeover and reappeared on shelves in 1994, as a crime-fighting, skateboarding, extreme sports fanatic with a new enemy in the form of Doctor X. These new toys had little in common with their forefathers, and in 2006 Action Man once again took a bow, and his line of toys was discontinued.

Other things to watch out for include a 1996 30th anniversary special edition Action Man, which was a reproduction of his first 1966 soldier appearance; a set of three 2004 GI Joe reproductions; and a range of 2006 Action Man 40th anniversary reproductions.

◄ Action Man sailor. 1970. (vg). Sold 14 August 2006: £150.10

► Royal Canadian Mounted Police. (1975). Unboxed. (g) Sold September 2009: £27.90

▲ Equipment Manual. 1974. (g-vg) Sold September 2009: £6.10

ADVERTISING

Advertising is a wide subject area that includes many different types of collectable items, such as postcards and posters (including reproductions), enamel signs, toys (including freebies), packaging, and even magazine cuttings. The range of subject matter also means that many advertising items have "dual appeal," meaning they would be of interest to more than one group of collectors. For example, a diecast model with a Kellogg's logo on the side would be of interest to advertising enthusiasts and also diecast model collectors.

With so many different items to choose from in this category, many collectors will choose to specialise: Some might collect milk bottles with adverts printed on the side, while others might only collect postcards. In particular, there is huge demand for old enamelled advertising signs; so much so that some astute entrepreneurs have built successful businesses making reproductions of them. The difference between a reproduction and an original is generally easy to distinguish as years of wear and tear (particularly when exposed to the elements) are normally obvious. Originals can command hundreds of pounds and can be found at collectors' fairs, autojumbles and car boot sales.

▲ Unigate Milk bottle. (1985). (vg). Sold March 2011: £4.10

▲ Lyons enamel sign. (1945). 450 x 300mm. (g). Sold September 2010: £43.60

Storage is a drawback, as advertising signs can take up quite a large amount of space (at least they can be affixed to walls).

Some collectors will go so far as to focus their collection to only a specific brand. Popular choices are the brands that made use of iconic images in their advertisements, such as Bisto and Fry's chocolate.

Stickers have often been used as a form of advertising, particularly in transport-related industries, and there is a market for examples in good condition. The biggest problem with stickers is that, in most cases, they can only be used once. After they have been stuck to something, it is very difficult to remove and remount them without causing damage. For this reason, it can be difficult to find stickers in good, unused condition. If a sticker has been removed from its original backing it will be worth significantly less than if it has not been used or tampered with, and this is worth bearing in mind when traversing your local boot sale.

▲ Platignum Pens tin sign. (1965). 320 x 245mm. (vg). Sold May 2006: £15.10

▲ Johnnie Walker calendar. (1960). (vg). Sold January 2010: £30.10

▲ Riley 1.5 Advertising Brochure. 1959. (vg). Sold April 2010: £18.10

▲ Berry's Diamond boot polish postcard. 1908. (g). Sold March 2011: £18

▲ Newcastle Brown Ale tin sign. (1955). 610 x 388mm. (g). Sold 9 October 2006: £27.50

▲ Schweppes metal clock. (1970). 302 x 302mm. (vg). Sold November 2010: £14.10

▲ Woman's Realm advertising card. 1958. 380 x 245mm. (vg). Sold April 2010: £12.10

AERONAUTICA

Aeronautica is the term for items relating to airlines and aviation. This is a superb collecting area. There are plenty of small items available, meaning they are easy to store. There's an abundance of items available and plenty at very affordable prices. With so much material available, the clever collector has the luxury of picking and choosing.

▲ BOAC flight bag. (1960). (g). Sold January 2011: £15.40

One tip is to concentrate on airlines that no longer exist. For example, anything relating to BOAC is desirable. However, never forget the golden collecting rule that condition is very important. If you concentrate on one particular airline, you will be kept seriously busy and you can always upgrade your collection with better condition examples and trade your duplicates.

As surprising as it may seem, collecting sick bags is not that uncommon. Some collectors pick up any sick bags they can get, while others focus on collecting all the sick bags issued by a specific airline. Often sick bags are issued with spelling mistakes or misprints, and there is a growing market for these too.

▲ BEA postcard. 1954. (g-vg). Sold November 2010: £10

Perhaps the most desirable aeronautica is anything relating to Concorde.

With many airlines either going out of business or changing their names, it pays to collect just about anything that is on offer at a very low price and, of course, you should always save your own airline tickets and related items, ensuring you keep them in mint condition.

▲ Air Atlantique Douglas DC3 model. 1998. (ex). Sold January 2010: £25.10

▲ British Airways beer mat. (1980). (vg). Sold March 2010: £5.20

◄ Concorde First Day Cover. 1969. (vg). Sold February 2011: £12.60

▲ Flight International magazine. 1962. (g).
Sold January 2011: £2.60

▲ NATO Open Day programme. 1971. (g).
Sold February 2011: £4.60

▲ Court Line ticket. 1971. (g-vg). Sold August 2010:
£2.10

▲ BEA cap badge. (1950). (vg). Did not
sell at £25 start price in February 2011.

▲ International Air Tattoo sticker. 1983.
(vg). Sold January 2011: £1

▲ Commercial Aircraft (book). 1978. (vg).
Sold September 2010: £5.10

AIRFIX

Airfix was founded in 1939 by a Hungarian called Nicholas Kove. The company originally sold inflatable toys, but moved into the field of model kits in 1949. The first aircraft kit was not made until 1955.

▲ Bristol Bulldog. (1965). (g).
Sold February 2009: £15.10

▲ BAC Aerospatiale Concorde. 1988. (ex).
Sold April 2008: £32

▲ Tank. (1960). (ex).
Sold June 2009: £10.10

▲ Russian infantry. 2000. (vg).
Sold September 2009: £7.90

ANNUALS

As with all collectables, the subject matter is the most important factor when determining which annuals to buy. For example, a Roy Rogers annual will generally be more desirable to a collector than a Pokémon annual.

When considering the condition of an annual, there are two particularly important things to bear in mind: spine and price clipping. Annuals that have been price clipped (look for a snipped off corner on one of the first few pages) will be devalued. Spine condition is of the utmost importance, as a poor spine can result in pages coming loose or being lost.

Many annuals include puzzle pages. These can be crosswords, word searches, spot the difference competitions, or something similar (in Blue Peter annuals, there were usually "Mystery Pictures" which children were encouraged to colour in with felt tip pens). Because of the nature of these pages, quite often you will find they have been scribbled on, which will obviously reduce the value of the annual considerably. Always check the condition of puzzle pages to make sure they have not been completed, or at worst have been completed with pencil crayons rather than ink.

▲ Tiger. 1957. (f).
Sold February 2011: £10.10

▲ The Boys' Own Paper. 1889. (g).
Sold February 2011: £27.00

▲ Worzel Gummidge. 1983. (vg).
Sold November 2010: £5.10

▲ Radio Fun. 1960. (f-g).
Sold November 2010: £10.20

▲ Look-in. 1975. (g).
Sold November 2010: £10.60

▲ Buffalo Bill. 1955. (g).
Sold November 2010: £8.30

▲ The Girl from U.N.C.L.E. 1969.
(vg). Sold July 2010: £15.10

▲ TV Comic. 1975. (g).
Sold February 2011: £3

▲ Photoplay Film Annual. 1971. (g).
Sold June 2010: £5.20

▲ Eagle. 1965. (g).
Sold June 2010: £5.20

▲ Picture Show. 1950. (g).
Sold June 2010: £10.10

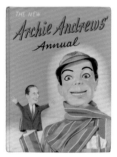

▲ The New Archie Andrews' Annual.
1958. (vg). Sold March 2010: £26.10

AUTOGRAPHS

▲ Count Basie. No dedication. Sold January 2011: £100

▲ Peggy Lee. Dedicated. Sold January 2011: £80

▲ Benny Hill. Dedicated. Sold November 2010: £26.70

Before you start buying autographs you really do need to do your homework. Sadly, the advent of internet auctions has created a vast market for forgers. Some experts now believe that more than 50% of autographs offered for sale on the internet are forgeries.

Many famous people now realise that autographs are not always sought by true fans, but by people who simply want to sell the autograph online; as a result, more celebrities are inclined to use pre-printed autographs, or autographs produced by an autopen.

Many pre-prints (also known as facsimiles) are done so well that they look as though they have been written personally in ink. There is actually nothing wrong with having such autographs in a collection, as long as they were not purchased under the belief that they were genuine. Examining a pre-print under a magnifying glass will often reveal the dots produced by the printing process, so this is a good test to see if a signature is real or not.

The process of using an autopen involves the celebrity signing just once. The autopen machine then recreates the signing motion, reproducing the original signature hundreds or even thousands of times in real pen. These are much more difficult to detect than pre-prints, but sometimes white flecks can be seen under a magnifying glass. Autopens are also usually very neat, because the celebrity will have taken time when signing the original to get a good copy.

The best way to identify an autopen is to compare it to other examples. Discovering an absolutely identical signature is a sure sign it is not original.

In the past, signatures were sometimes reproduced with a rubber stamp. Smudges on the autograph can make them easy to spot.

The best advice when buying is to use the services of an established professional dealer. Such traders will normally have a shop or office premises open to the public. It is worth paying a little more for peace of mind.

Dealers will usually supply a certificate of authenticity; but remember that such certificates are easy to produce, and may not be worth the paper they are printed on.

Provenance can add value to an autograph. This is where some sort of evidence accompanies the autograph, helping to prove it is genuine. Such evidence can include a photograph of the famous person signing the autograph, or a letter.

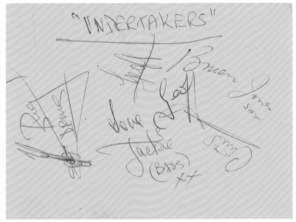

▲ The Undertakers. No dedication. Sold November 2010: £100

▲ Anton Diffring. No dedication. Sold September 2010: £24.40

▲ Lauren Bacall. No dedication. Sold June 2010: £75

▲ Morecambe & Wise. Dedicated. Sold August 2010: £40.40

▲ Britney Spears. No dedication. Sold June 2010: £100.30

▲ Leonard Rossiter. No dedication. Sold August 2010: £50.10

AUTOMOBILIA

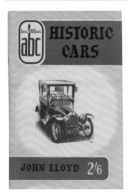

▲ Historic Cars (book). 1957. (vg). Sold January 2011: £3

Automobilia is a massive subject area that encompasses several other collecting topics such as AA, petroliana (items relating to the petrol industry), diecast models, tax discs, and books (all of which are covered in their own categories throughout this book). Because of this, items of automobilia often appeal to several different types of collectors and therefore stand a good chance of selling for decent prices when put up for auction.

Some automobilia enthusiasts will collect anything they can find, but many more will focus on a particular brand. Brands that no longer exist will obviously be popular, and these can demand the highest sums.

▲ The Motor magazine (London Motorshow edition). 1957. (g-vg). Sold June 2010: £20.10

Many items in this category, such as spare car parts, machinery from workshops, and signs from old garages, can be quite large and heavy. This is something that should be considered when building a collection: you need somewhere to store your treasures, and should you decide to sell them, you need to factor postage and packing costs into your prices.

▲ Mini Owners Manual. 1983. (f-g). Sold September 2010: £2

It is also worth noting that automobilia items can often be rather grubby. As always, clean items in excellent condition will command a premium, but a certain amount of grime, wear and tear is acceptable for rarer pieces.

One of the popular collectable subjects in this category is car instruction manuals. These books are not only a fascinating snapshot of motoring from the past, but can also be useful for anyone who actually owns and maintains that particular model of vehicle. As already mentioned, such books were generally kept in the garage and are likely to be a bit creased and soiled; so good condition examples are not always easy to find and will be more desirable, although poor examples should still find a market.

▲ Driving instructor enamel sign. (1955). (g). Sold March 2010: £37.60

▲ Rolls-Royce spanner. (1965). (vg). Sold September 2010: £3.30

▲ Motoring goggles. (1935). (f-g). Sold July 2010: £15.20

▲ Shell Historic Cars coin collection. (1970). (vg). Sold September 2010: £15

▲ Camping Club grille badge. (1965). (ex). Sold March 2010: £21.20

▲ Ford accessories leaflet. 1959. (vg). Sold March 2010: £4.70

◀ Malta car grille badge. (1970). (g-vg). Sold January 2011: £5

▲ MG Group enamel badge. (1975). (ex). Sold July 2010: £5.10

▲ Mercedes bonnet badge. (1960). (g). Sold February 2011: £10

▲ Rover hood ornament. (1960). (g). Sold June 2010: £15.70

AVON

Quite a few people collect Avon items, but mainly perfume bottles, ceramics, and novelty decanters. There is not a huge market for other Avon products such as appliances and make-up, and it is important to do your homework before investing large amounts of money. Remember, just because some items relating to a specific company have increased in value, this does not mean that all of the items relating to that company will increase in value in the same way.

▲ Avon light bulb soap. (1975). (vg). Sold January 2010: £3

▲ Bloodhound Avon bottle. (1975). (vg). Sold June 2008: £8.70

▲ Andy Capp Avon bottle. 1969. (vg). Sold February 2011: £30.10

BABYCHAM

In the 1940s, the Showering brothers (Arthur, Herbert, Ralph and Francis) ran a small brewery at their Shepton Mallet site. They concentrated on mineral water and cider, eventually making the pear cider Babycham.

Initially tested in the local area, the drink proved very popular. After a short period of selling the drink in large bottles, they started selling it in the (now extremely famous) green 'baby' bottles. The drink was entered into competitions at many agricultural shows across the country and regularly won first prize, earning it the nickname 'Baby Champ.'

Following a very successful national launch in 1953, it became the first ever alcoholic drinks brand to be advertised on commercial television in the UK. It was originally advertised as "Genuine Champagne Perry" and adverts featured Bambi, the iconic yellow deer with an oversized blue bow tie.

▲ Babycham tea towel. (1965). (vg). Sold 14 August 2006: £35.30

Production was increased dramatically and the drink was proving successful worldwide. It was heavily marketed towards women, with pioneering television advertisements helping to increase the appeal of the brand.

A change in the country's drinking habits and a significantly increased amount of competition meant Babycham's popularity waned in the late 1970s and it was regularly mocked on television during the 80s.

▲ Plastic Bambi figure. (1965). (g-vg).Sold 21 March 2005: £21.60

▲ Babycham plastic deer. (1965). (vg). Sold 26 July 2007: £22.90

The brand was modernised in 1993, and the famous deer image was removed in order to appeal to a new generation. However, after only three years, the deer was reinstated as part of a huge re-launch. A lot of media attention helped and, once again, there was a significant amount of interest in the brand.

Since 1953, Babycham has manufactured a wide range of items intended to advertise the brand. Lots of these have now become highly sought after by collectors.

Collectors of breweriana tend to collect anything related to a particular brewery (including old advertising signs, glasses and beer mats). However, it is definitely worth looking out for more unusual items as these may command a premium when sold (due to their rarity).

Of particular interest to Babycham collectors is the Pirelli Babycham glass figure, which can be worth in excess of £70 if in good condition.

Original items from the 50s and 60s will generally command higher sums when sold. Collectors will be especially interested in items dating from the national launch in 1953 and even more interested in any items advertising the product before its national launch. However, this does not mean modern items are not worthy of collecting, as some most certainly are.

▲ Babycham Glass. (1975). (vg). Sold April 2010: £10

▲ Advertising display card. 1996. (vg). Sold 23 August 2007: £4.60

Babycham was often served in a special glass. At the height of its popularity, these glasses were a regular sight in pubs up and down the country, meaning there are now a large number of these glasses available at car boot sales and fairs, often at reasonable prices (aim to pay £1 - £2). Other items that you should find fairly easily include beer mats and ashtrays. Although these are common examples, meaning their value will obviously be less, they certainly do make a lovely addition to a themed collection. Also, if the Babycham brand continues to increase in popularity, there will be even more demand for these older collectables in the future, meaning they may offer good investment potential.

Over more than 60 years, many bars and pubs have displayed a number of different posters and signs on their walls, all of which are now very interesting to a collector. Obviously, condition is crucial and a poster in excellent condition will be worth a lot more than a poster that has been stuck on a dirty pub wall for the last 30 years. Some pubs also had some interesting items (including clocks and mirrors) that are well worth looking out for.

▲ Babycham beer mat. (1965). (g). Sold February 2008: £7.10

BADGES

Collecting badges can be lots of fun. A large collection can often be amassed for very little expense, and when framed, good quality examples will make wonderful display pieces. There is also a huge range of subjects to specialise in; but buy with care if you are intending to sell your badges for profit, as only certain makes and subject matters will have a strong investment potential.

A good tip is to find a stallholder at a boot sale who is selling lots of badges, and make an offer for his or her entire stock. Buying in bulk, you should get a good price; then you can sort through the hoard at your leisure, picking out the best badges to sell individually for higher sums.

▲ T E Lawrence Society badge (Fattorini). (1985). (g).Sold June 2006: £2

One particular make to watch out for is Fattorini, one of the most famous badge manufacturers. The company was founded by Antonio Fattorini, an Italian immigrant, who settled in Yorkshire in 1827.

One of the most popular badge themes is Butlin's, and more about this specialised collecting area can be found later in this book.

Also look out for club badges, such as those issued by the Buzby Junior (Post Office Telecommunications) Club, and the Tufty Club. Tufty was a squirrel, and the star of a series of public information films designed to promote road safety for children. He was so popular that at one point his club had over two million members. The badges issued to club members are now very desirable.

▲ Buzby Junior Club badge. (1978). (vg). Sold March 2010: £5.30

▲ Tufty Club badge. (1960). (vg). Sold January 2010: £5.10

▲ TGWU Shop Steward enamel badge. (1965). 30 x 26mm. (vg). Sold April 2011: £3

▲ Belle Vue Zoo badge. (1960). 26mm diam. (vg). Sold April 2011: £10.10

▲ British Legion Women's Section badge. (1935). (ex). Sold June 2010: £14.80

▲ World Cup Willie badge. 1966. (vg). Sold April 2010: £40.10

▲ Hull Speedway badge. 1977. (vg). Sold August 2010: £3

BANKNOTES (BRITISH)

Collecting banknotes is an incredibly specialised field, and it is not recommended to spend serious money unless you first know what you are doing. Do your homework, then buy with confidence, and give yourself a chance of making an investment.

Store your banknotes flat and never fold them. Take particular care with the corners. Values depend on rarity and condition. A scruffy note is worth a fraction of a mint/excellent example. Sadly, not all notes being sold on the internet or at car boot sales are going to be genuine. Be absolutely satisfied before buying.

It is important to store your banknotes where they will not get wet and will not fade (i.e. out of direct sunlight, in a cool, dry location). It may be worth investing in specially-made banknote folders that will keep your notes free from environmental damage.

Valuable notes include those that are no longer in circulation, such as the "white fiver" and the £1 note. Interestingly, the first printed £1 note was introduced in 1797 to release gold and silver to fight the Napoleonic War. The last £1 note was printed in 1984.

▲ "White fiver". 1956. (ex). Sold 26 July 2007: £135.90

▲ £1 note. 1984. (mnt). Sold October 2005: £11.10

BANKNOTES (WORLD)

World banknotes are a good example of a collecting area that can be started at very low cost. Many banknotes are attractively designed, giving the collection a pleasing look. This is also a great collecting idea for children, helping promote an interest in world history and geography.

Much research would be required before embarking on this hobby with serious money. Find cheap foreign banknotes at some charity shops (particularly Oxfam specialist shops). There are plenty of notes on the internet, but do tread carefully, and don't be tempted to overspend.

Some years ago, The Sunday Times gave away various world banknotes with their magazine. Needless to say they had very low face values. These are constantly cropping up and are worth only pennies.

It is always worth holding onto any banknotes for countries that have since converted to the Euro. The obsolete notes could well prove highly collectable one day.

▲ 20 Schillings - Austria. 1956. (g). Sold November 2008: £5.10

▲ 1000 Manat - Azerbaijan. (1993). (f). Sold May 2008: £4.10

▲ 10 Francs - Belgium. 1943. (f-g). Sold November 2008: £5.10

▲ 10 Lev - Bulgaria. 1974. (ex-mnt). Sold September 2008: £5.10

▲ 5 Colones - Costa Rica. 1989. (g-vg). Sold June 2008: £2.50

▲ 10 Korun - Czechoslovakia. 1986. (g). Sold September 2008: £4

▲ £1 - Eire. 1989. (f). Sold November 2008: £3.10

▲ 1 Kroon - Estonia. 1992. (vg). Sold November 2008: £3.10

▲ 50 Francs - France. 1993. (vg). Sold November 2008: £5.10

▲ 50 Drachmai - Greece. 1978. (f-g). Sold May 2008: £5

▲ 100 Forint - Hungary. 1992. (g). Sold June 2008: £4.10

▲ 100 Escudos - Mozambique. 1976. (ex). Sold May 2008: £4.10

▲ 1 Centavo - Nicaragua. 1991. (ex). Sold May 2008: £4.10

▲ 1000 Lira - Turkey. 1970. (g-vg). Sold September 2008: £4

▲ 1000 Dong - Vietnam. 1988. (g-vg). Sold September 2008: £4.60

▲ 50 Kwacha - Zambia. 1986-1988. (ex). Sold June 2008: £6

BEANIE BABIES

▲ Amber Beanie Baby. 1999. (vg). Sold 26 July 2007: £8.00

▲ Groovy. 1999. (vg). Sold January 2010: £1.90

▲ Tiny Chihuahua Beanie Baby. 1998. (ex). Sold 20 February 2006: £8.10

Beanie Babies were the brainchild of Ty Warner, founder of Ty Inc., who was born 3 September 1944.

Ty had formed his company in 1986, using inheritance money and his life savings to get started, but it was not until 1993 that he hit upon the idea of small plush toys that children could afford to buy with their pocket money and carry around with them. The first two Beanie Babies appeared early in 1993, with a series of nine being revealed later that same year at the World Toy Fair in New York City. Surprisingly, they were not an immediate hit, with some critics at the Fair referring to them as "roadkill" because of their under-stuffed, slightly flattened appearance.

▲ Specs Beanie Kids Beanie Baby. 2001. (ex). Sold 19 December 2005: £10.00

However, it did not take long for the toys to start being considered as collectables, and the market soared, mainly because each Beanie was available for a limited period only before being "retired." By the end of the 90s, the world was firmly in the grip of Beanie Baby mania, with some determined collectors paying hundreds of pounds for a single Beanie. With so many people buying up the toys, envisioning huge profits later on, it was only a matter of time before the bubble burst, and it is unfortunately the case that many people who heavily invested in collections of Beanies will never recoup their expenses.

▲ Russia 2002 FIFA World Cup bear. (vg). Sold January 2010: £3

The Beanie Baby story is a timely reminder to all of us that we can never truly predict market trends. Some items are destined to be "fads" that eventually go out of fashion, and it takes a steady nerve and a quick eye to be able to hop in and out of the market at the right time to make a profit without being stung if the prices eventually crash.

▲ Prance. 1997. (vg). Sold January 2010: £2

BEATLES

▲ Tour programme. 1964. (vg). Sold January 2010: £52.10

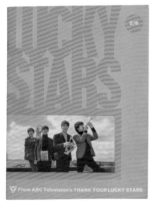

▲ Lucky Stars book. 1963. (vg).Sold April 2010: £19

In March 1957, John Lennon formed a skiffle group called The Quarrymen. Lennon met Paul McCartney at a garden fête in July 1957, and McCartney was invited to join the group. In February 1958, George Harrison was invited to watch the group perform (Paul had met George on the morning school bus), and he joined the band a month later. In August 1960, the band was renamed The Beatles. Ringo Starr completed the Fab Four when he replaced Pete Best in 1962.

▲ Long Tall Sally EP. 1964. (vg). Sold June 2010: £16.10

When searching around your local car boot sale, just about any Beatles memorabilia you find that dates from the '60s is worth snapping up (at the right price, of course). Most items are priced higher than the average boot treasure but still often below true value.

Be aware that there is a lot of Beatles merchandise around, but not all of it is official. Unofficial products usually have a smaller distribution and are therefore more difficult to find. Surprisingly, this means that sometimes unofficial products can be more desirable to a collector.

▲ Love Me Do picture disc. 1982. (vg). Sold June 2010: £15.10

▲ Beatle Convention badges. 1981. (g). Sold April 2010: £6.10 each

▲ New Sound Guitar. (1964). (g-vg). Sold June 2010: £135.70

BEER MATS

▲ Giant Babycham beer mat (front and back). (1990). (g). Sold May 2008: £2.30

The collecting of beer mats is known as tegestology. It is a collecting area that is often overlooked by traders. As such, prices at the moment tend to be rather low, and this is something we should all be taking advantage of.

▲ Double Diamond beer mat. (1975). (g). Sold July 2010: £2.30

To maximise investment potential, look out for interesting old examples in excellent, clean condition. Beer mats cut into unusual shapes are popular, as are mats for drink brands that no longer exist.

Even if you are not specifically collecting beer mats, they are still worth seeking out at collectors' fairs and boot sales (where they can often be bought in large quantities at low prices) because they can be added to different themed collections. For example; a Babycham beer mat is a valuable and interesting addition to a themed Babycham collection.

▲ Hennessy beer mat. (1960). (vg). Sold May 2010: £1.50

▲ Worthington Green Shield beer mat. (1960). (vg). Sold May 2010: £2.60

▲ Flowers Brewmaster beer mat. (1960). (vg). Sold May 2010: £1.50

▲ Mackeson Stout beer mat. (1960). (vg). Sold May 2010: £1

▲ Schweppes beer mat. (1975). (g). Sold March 2010: £5.10

▲ Andy Capp beer mat. 1996. (f). Sold February 2011: £4.30

BILLHEADS

Originally, bills (invoices) were handwritten. In the nineteenth century, printing processes included copperplate and steel engravings, enabling tasteful, original and decorative designs to be displayed on billheads. By 1925, the practice was starting to recede.

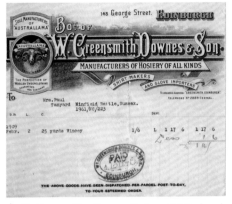

▲ W Greensmiths Downes & Son. 1909. (g-vg). Sold April 2008: £6.20

▲ Kibbe Brothers Co. 1897. (ex). Sold February 2005: £10.10

BLUE PETER

▲ Blue Peter Book 2. 1966. (f). Sold September 2008: £5.10

▲ Blue Peter Book 4. 1968. (g). Sold March 2008: £10.10

Blue Peter memorabilia can usually be expected to find a market. The famous Blue Peter badges and autographs are particularly desirable although they are not always that easy to come by.

Annuals can be easily found at car boot sales and many are at sensible prices. Condition is vitally important. Be patient and look for undamaged examples. For an annual in average condition, you should be looking to pay 50p - £1. The exception to this is Book 1, which commands considerably higher sums. Numbers 2 - 25 are not particularly hard to find, but higher numbers start to become more difficult.

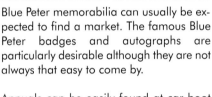

▲ Blue Peter Book 5: 1969. Sold September 2008: £4.50

▲ Mark, Caron, and Yvette autographs. No dedication. Sold March 2010: £45.10

▲ Phonecard. 1993. (g). Sold September 2010: £3.10

BOOKMARKS

Bookmarks are fascinating collectables. They are easy to store and transport, and many make very attractive display items. Bookmarks featuring advertisements are some of the most desirable.

▲ Stourbridge Voluntary Services bookmark. 1963. (vg). Sold December 2008: £3

▲ Douglas and Foulis bookmark. (1920). (g). Sold December 2008: £10.10

▲ Northern Assurance Company bookmark. 1909. (vg). Sold December 2008: £10.10

▲ The Great Brown Owl bookmark. (1920). (vg). Sold May 2008: £11.10

▲ Ernest Hemingway Penguin bookmark. (1975). (vg). Sold May 2008: £5.10

▲ Royal Exchange Assurance bookmark. (1900). (g). Sold May 2008: £5.10

▲ Guardian Assurance bookmark. (1910). (f). Sold September 2009: £5.10

▲ Butterfly bookmark. (1975). (vg). Sold June 2008: £5

BOOKS

Obviously, book collecting is a rather broad subject area, and most collectors will focus on a particular aspect, such as author, theme, or publishing house. Interest in rare and antiquarian books is growing fast, and first editions are often the most valued items in a collection

Many collectors would argue that there is no point having a collection of books if you can't enjoy reading them. Books found at car boot sales are likely to be "reading copies;" books that are not rare enough or in good enough condition to have significant investment potential. If you are going to handle your real treasures, then do so carefully. Make sure you have clean hands and open pages slowly, being particularly careful not to bend or crack the spines of paperback editions. If you know a book has loose pages, then be extra cautious, as you don't want them to start falling out of the spine. Whatever you do, don't eat while looking through a book, and don't lick your fingers to turn the pages; nobody wants books full of stains and crumbs. If you must use a bookmark, use an extra thin one that will not deform the pages.

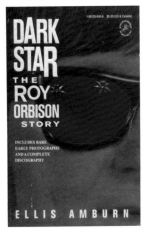

▲ Dark Star: The Roy Orbison Story (paperback). 1991. (g-vg). Sold July 2010: £20.10

▲ Our Air Force (hardback). 1940. (f).Sold February 2011: £10.20

▲ Around the World in 25 Years (paperback). 1984. (vg). Sold March 2010: £5.60

▲ Biggles of the Camel Squadron (paperback). 1977. (vg). Sold March 2010: £2.60

▲ The Adventures of Carlo (hardback). (1910). (g-vg). Sold November 2010: £8.10

▲ Whiplash (paperback). 1952. (g). Sold March 2010: £5.70

BOTTLE OPENERS

Although bottle openers are becoming more collectable, it is an area where there is not a huge amount of interest at the moment. Corkscrews are slowly becoming obsolete with the increasing popularity of screw caps, and this could lead to an increase in value.

▲ Double Diamond bottle opener. (1965). (g). Sold April 2008: £10

▲ Metal corkscrew. (1970). (f). Sold March 2008: £5.20

▲ Seymour's bottle opener. (1945). (g). Sold April 2008: £8.30

▲ Watneys bottle opener. (1970). (g). Sold March 2009: £5.20

BOTTLES

Bottle collecting is an inexpensive hobby that attracts people for a number of reasons. Many bottles have product/company names on them, which appeals to people who collect products from certain companies. Some bottle collectors also purchase bottles to use as attractive ornaments. For some people part of the enjoyment of this hobby is digging up the bottles but, if you haven't got the time for this, you can often find them at car boot sales for reasonable prices.

An interesting sub-category is collecting poison bottles. After 1870 poison bottles were designed to be easily identifiable by touch. They would have a raised surface, with ridges and lines, and embossed lettering, so they could be identified in the dark. Poison bottles were usually dark blue, green, or amber, with blue being the most common. Clear and light coloured poison bottles are quite rare.

▲ Green poison bottle. (1920). (vg). Sold September 2008: £3.60

▲ Stoneware bottle. (1910). (vg). Sold March 2010: £4.10

▲ Codd-neck bottle. (1890). (vg). Sold March 2010: £8.90

BOWLS

This is a very specialist area, and it can be difficult to find enough interested parties to start a bidding war. Some of the most common and desirable collectables are enamel badges.

▲ Carmarthen County Bowling Association badge. (1960). (vg). Sold March 2010: £2.30

▲ Essex County Indoor Bowling Club badge. (1970). (vg). Sold March 2010: £2.30

▲ Bedford Borough Bowling Club badge. (1970). (vg). Sold March 2010: £2.30

▲ Warwickshire Bowling Association badge. (1960). (vg). Sold March 2010: £3.20

▲ Milford Haven Bowling Club badge. (1970). (vg). Sold March 2010: £2.30

▲ Pembroke County Bowling Association badge. (1970). (vg). Sold March 2010: £2.30

▲ Isle of Wight Bowling Association badge. (1960). (vg). Sold March 2010: £2.30

▲ Whitstable Bowling Club badge. (1970). (vg). Sold March 2010: £2.40

BOXING

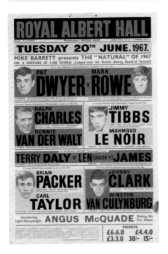

▲ Mickey Duff matchmaker bill poster. 1967. (vg). Sold February 2011: £40

There is quite a strong market for boxing memorabilia. Some of the easiest items to find are old magazines, autographed items, and programmes. Posters are much harder to find (as they were often torn, stained, or thrown away).

Arguably the most desirable items in this particular category are gloves and shorts worn by big-name stars, but such items do not come cheap, and proving they are genuine is not always easy. It is definitely a collecting subject where caution is recommended.

▲ Henry Cooper autographed picture. No dedication. Sold April 2010: £25.10

BREWERIANA

Breweriana is anything related to alcohol and the brewing industry. This includes beer mats, beer pump signs, advertising materials, jugs, tankards, glasses, ash trays, bottles, and much more. There is a huge selection, but remember that many breweriana items would have been used in public houses and may have suffered for it. Condition is of paramount importance.

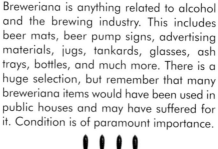

▲ Whyte & Mackay Whisky jug. (1975). (vg). Sold March 2011: £8

▲ Bulmer's plastic woodpecker model. (1965). (vg). Sold March 2010: £40.10

▲ Model of bar and beer pumps. (1975). 142 x 88 x 48mm. (vg). Sold November 2009: £16.30

▲ Wadworth Farmers Glory beer pump sign. (1975). (g). Sold May 2008: £2.10

▲ Martell Cognac jug. (1970). (ex). Sold April 2010: £18.10

▲ Henry's IPA beer pump sign. (1985). (g). Sold April 2010: £2

▲ Watneys Red Barrel keyring. (1960). (vg). Sold June 2009: £9.20

▲ Watneys ceramic mug. 1981. (vg-ex).Sold September 2007: £10

▲ Promotional whisky cask piece. 2005. (vg). Sold January 2010: £5.10

BUTLIN'S

▲ Butlin's Loyalty Club Badge Collection case (empty). (1990). (vg). Sold April 2011: £38.70

Billy Butlin (born in 1899) started his venture in the amusement park business with the purchase of a piece of land in Skegness. Four hoopla stalls, a tower slide, a homemade haunted house, and a small track for battery operated cars were the first attractions at the "Butlin's Amusement Site." By the 1930s, Billy had opened eight permanent amusement sites along the coast.

The first Butlin's holiday camp opened at Skegness on Easter Saturday 1936. The first season of the camp was oversubscribed, encouraging Billy to open more holiday camps. The next was Clacton (opened 1938).

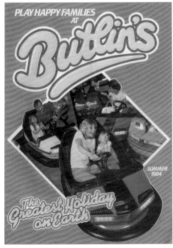

▲ Butlin's brochure. 1984. (vg). Sold November 2010: £20.10

▲ Skegness enamel badge. 1962. (vg). Sold July 2010: £10.10

▲ Margate enamel badge. 1958. (vg). Sold July 2010: £15.10

▲ Clacton enamel badge. 1961. (vg). Sold July 2010: £25.10

▲ Filey enamel badge. 1963. (g). Sold July 2010: £8.60

Two areas of Butlin's merchandise are by far the most popular: Badges and postcards. However, sometimes slightly more obscure items (such as a flask, or even a coat hanger) can prove to be the best things to hold on to, as less people actually acquired these items, meaning they are now harder to find.

As with all collectables, condition is very important to the value, so make sure you store your items very carefully.

▲ Brighton enamel badge. 1955. (g). Sold November 2009: £25

▲ Butlin Beavers Club badge. 1963. (vg). Sold September 2009: £6.30

BUTTONHOOKS

Buttonhooks were popular towards the end of the 19th century. They were implements used to make the tiresome task of undoing a multitude of buttons easier. They come in many sizes, from around 20 inches to less than an inch. The handles are also varied.

▲ Ebony handle buttonhook. 1920. (vg). Sold March 2008: £25.10

▲ Silver handle buttonhook. 1915. (g). Sold June 2008: £26.70

▲ Mother of pearl handle buttonhook. (1915). (vg). Sold July 2008: £7.60

CARTOPHILY

During the late 1800s it became common for cigarette manufacturers to put a "stiffener" card in paper packets. This was simply a blank card that was used to prevent the contents of the packet from being broken or bent. By the 1880s, American companies were using these cards for advertising purposes. The first British company to use "stiffeners" as advertising cards was WD & HO Wills, around 1888.

Several years later the advertising cards were replaced with general interest picture cards. To begin with, these cards were blank on the reverse, but eventually text was introduced.

The production of cards was ceased during both World Wars and once the Second World War was over, rationing and high production costs prevented a return to the era of mass cigarette card production.

Many releases of cigarette cards were produced with an accompa-

▲ Monkees (full set). 1967. (vg). Sold March 2010: £30.70

nying album in which to store them. The problem with these albums was, in most cases, it was necessary for the cards to be stuck in place, and this would invariably ruin them. For this reason, loose cards are often more desirable to collectors.

▲ Characters from Dickens (full set). 1912. (vg). Sold January 2010: £30.60

▲ Film, Stage & Radio Stars (full set). 1935. (vg-ex). Sold January 2010: £25.10

▲ Lucky Charms (full set). 1923. (vg-ex). Sold March 2010: £25.60

▲ Aviary and Cage Birds (full set). 1933. (vg-ex). Sold March 2010: £38.10

▲ British Birds and Their Eggs (single card). 1938. (f-g). Sold May 2010: £5.10

▲ Romance of the Heavens (full set). 1928. (g-vg). Sold May 2010: £20.10

▲ First Aid (full set). 1918. (g). Sold June 2010: £32

▲ Decorations and Medals (full set). (vg). Sold November 2010: £40.10

▲ Ships of All Ages (full set). 1929. (vg). Sold February 2011: £15.20

▲ Straight Line Caricatures (full set). 1926. (g-vg).Sold March 2010: £12.80

▲ Guns in Action (full set). 1938. (g). Sold May 2010: £10.60

▲ Amusing Tricks (full set). 1937. (vg). Sold August 2010: £40.10

CHEESE LABELS

The collecting of cheese labels is known as fromology. It was a popular collecting pastime in the 1950s.

▲ Rupp Kasle (Germany). (1970). (g-vg) Sold June 2009: £1

▲ Familie-Chasli (Switzerland). (1955). (vg) Sold June 2009: £1

▲ Golden Vale (Eire). (1960). (g) Sold June 2009: £1

▲ Handelsonderneming Rozee (Holland). (1955). (g-vg) Sold June 2009: £1

CHURCHILLIANA

▲ Winston Churchill autograph. No dedication. Sold December 2008: £650

Sir Winston Leonard Spencer Churchill was born on 30 November 1874. He was a British politician known chiefly for his leadership of Great Britain during World War II (he was Prime Minister from 1940 to 1945 and again from 1951 to 1955). He was also a prolific author, winning the Nobel Prize in Literature in 1953.

On 15 January 1965, he suffered a stroke. He died nine days later, aged 90, exactly 70 years after his father's death. Upon his death, the Queen granted him the honour of a state funeral, which saw one of the largest assemblies of statesmen in the world.

Items relating to Churchill are known as Churchilliana, and there is plenty of demand for interesting examples.

▲ Newspaper reporting Churchill's death. 25 Jan 1965. (f). Sold April 2008: £10

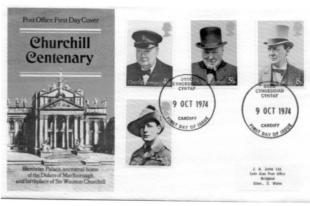

▲ Churchill First Day Cover. 9 Oct 1974. (vg). Sold December 2008: £17

CIGARETTE PACKETS

▲ Kenilworth No.20 Cigarettes. (1940). (g) Sold Nov 2009: £2.10

▲ Four Square Cigarettes. (1945). (g) Sold Nov 2009: £2.10

▲ The "Greys" Silk Cut. (1940). (g-vg) Sold Nov 2009: £2.50

▲ Craven "A" Virginia Cigarettes. (1950). (g-vg) Sold Nov 2009: £3

▲ Army Club, Sandhurst Size. (1940). (vg) Sold Nov 2009: £3.60

▲ Player's Airman Cigarettes. (1945) (f) Sold Nov 2009: £3

Collectors of cigarette packets generally prefer to collect "live" packs. These are packs that contain the original cigarettes. The packets themselves comprise the "hull" (the outsider of the packet) and "slide" (the section inside the packet that slides in and out).

The aim of any cigarette packet collector is to find good condition "live" packets, but as one might expect, these are particularly difficult to acquire.

The first health warning to be printed on cigarette packets appeared in 1971 and stated: "Warning by H.M. Government. Smoking can damage your health." In 1976, it also became mandatory to display the cigarette tar content. Since then, the warnings have been regularly updated, and this can prove very helpful when dating cigarette packets.

Unsurprisingly, it can be difficult to find old cigarette packets in mint condition. Some collectors focus on collecting cigerette packet fronts such as the ones illustrated on the left. These are generally cheaper than full packets but can look just as nice on display.

▲ Star. (1935). (g) Sold May 2009: £8

▲ Wild Woodbine. (1960). (g-vg) Sold May 2009: £3.30

▲ Black Cat. (1935). (p-f) Sold May 2009: £10.30

▲ Piccadilly. (1940). (g-vg) Sold May 2009: £12

CINEMA

▲ Cinema Clubs annual. (1949). (g-vg). Sold June 2005: £30

▲ The River's Edge poster.1957. (g). Sold November 2006: £25.10

▲ Odeon cinema enamel badge. (1940). (f). Sold August 2005: £25

▲ The Likely Lads lobby card. 1976. (vg). Sold November 2010: £6.20

▲ The Illustrated Man lobby card. 1951. (vg). Sold November 2010: £2

▲ Up the Chastity Belt lobby card. 1971. (vg). Sold November 2010: £3

CIRCUS

▲ Chipperfield's Circus crane (Corgi). 1963-1969. (vg-ex). Sold August 2010: £105.60

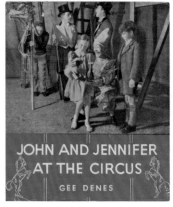

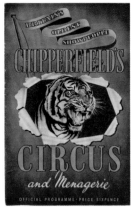

▲ Mills admission ticket. January 1949. (g-vg). Sold June 2009: £30

▲ John and Jennifer at the Circus (book). 1949. (vg). Sold June 2009: £40

▲ Chipperfield's programme. (1955). (g-vg). Sold March 2010: £25

COMICS

▲ Comet. 17 June 1950. (g-vg). Sold May 2010: £10.40

▲ Superman. November 1990. (vg). Sold November 2010: £2.30

When you collect comics, you are collecting a piece of social history. Comics were hugely popular before the advent of television, and they give a fascinating insight to political and cultural views of the time.

It is important to note that it is almost impossible to find a mint condition comic on the secondary market. The term mint condition should really only be used for comics that have covers that are not creased, faded, or even slightly curved. Furthermore, the spine of the comic should be straight and the staples should be free from rust. Inside, there should be no tears, folds, cuts, stains, or pen marks (except for autographs), and there should be no discolouration, fading, or foxing.

Issue one of any comic will obviously be in big demand and will have good investment potential. For example, in February 2010, a copy of Action Comics issue one (featuring the debut appearance of Superman) was sold in America for $1 million. Many first issues also came with a free gift, and if this gift is still present then the price will be further increased.

▲ Battle. 2 December 1978. (vg). Sold September 2010: £2.60

▲ The Magnet. 18 March 1922. (g-vg). Sold May 2010: £8.10

▲ Star Wars Weekly. Issue one, 1 Feb.1978. No gift. (vg). Sold June 2009: £26.90

▲ Whoopee! and Shiver & Shake. 27 September 1975. (vg). Sold September 2010: £2.10

▲ The Champion. September 1951. (g-vg). Sold June 2009: £5

COMPACTS

One of the most popular compact manufacturers is Stratton. Unfortunately, dating a Stratton compact is not easy. Here are some guidelines that can be helpful:

If the compact has a self-opening inner lid (patented by Stratton in 1948) then it means it was made after 1948. If the compact is convertible, or takes cream powder, then it dates from the 1950s. If the compact has the "Compact in Hand" logo on the inner lid, then it was made between 1950 and 1970.

▲ Stratton compact. (1935). (g). Sold February 2009: £23

▲ Yardley silverplated compact. (1935). (g). Sold March 2009: £38.10

▲ Coty vibrant compact. (1935). (g). Sold March 2009: £16

CONFECTIONERY

▲ Milky Way wrapper. (1975). (g). Sold May 2005: £8.70

Confectionery is something that many collectors may initially overlook, thereby missing out on a wealth of collecting opportunities. Always remember that when a big movie such as Lord of the Rings or Harry Potter is released, there will be plenty of merchandise released with it. As well as the video and board games, action figures, books, and other paraphernalia, you can be sure there will also be sweets and chocolates with specially branded packaging. Always check the sweet counter so as not to miss out on any collectables.

▲ Cadbury's chocolates box. (1940). (g). Sold February 2008: £6.10

▲ Jaffa Cakes Express tin. (1980). (g). Sold August 2006: £23.60

The most desirable confectionery items are packages and advertising for products or companies that no longer exist. Also, anything bearing the old name for a product that has been rebranded will be of interest (for example, a Marathon bar wrapper).

CRESTED CHINA

▲ Hamilton cheese platter. (1975). (vg). Sold March 2011: £6.10

▲ Eastbourne. (1980). (g). Sold June 2008: £12.60

▲ Isle of Wight. (1980). (vg). Sold June 2008: £3

▲ Edinburgh cheese platter. (1975). (vg). Sold March 2011: £5.00

CRICKET

▲ England v Australia cricket programme. July 1985. (g-vg). Sold June 2009. £5.10

▲ The Test Match Career of Geoffrey Boycott (hardback book). 1986. (vg). Sold March 2010: £5.10

▲ Yorkshire County Cricket Club Annual Report. 1957. (vg). Sold March 2009: £15

◀ Gunn & Moore cricket bat. Genuine autographs on both sides from the Gloucestershire team, Nottinghamshire team, Leicestershire team, Young England XI team, and the 1973 West Indies team (including Captain Rohan Kanhai, Vice Captain Lance Gibbs, and wicketkeeper Deryck Murray). (vg) Sold March 2009: £65

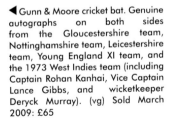

▲ Test Match cricket game. (1955). (g). Sold March 2010: £17.70

DEXTERITY PUZZLES

A dexterity puzzle is a handheld game, usually involving the careful rolling of ball bearings into small holes that are positioned within colourful designs.

The games became popular towards the end of the nineteenth century. The market was quickly cornered by Robert Journet, a London toy shop owner. Robert's father made the puzzles by hand.

The trouble is that these puzzles were not originally purchased with the view to storing them in the hope that mint condition examples would become serious investments. Consequently they were much played with and finding puzzles in excellent condition now is rather difficult.

Robert Journet died around 1935 and the business was taken over by his son Frederick. The business was eventually sold in 1965 to Abbey Corinthian Games.

Nice old examples are becoming increasingly popular with collectors and they are commanding more and more money. If you find one at a boot sale for £1 or so, then snap it up fast. Realistically, you are not going to find many Journets at boot sales. You will find a steady supply on internet auction websites but at much, much more than boot sale prices.

▲ The Pondsnag Puzzle (R. Journet). (1950). (f-g). Sold July 2010: £7.30

▲ Golden Rod puzzle (R. Journet). (1950). (g-vg). Sold August 2007: £12.10

▲ Pin-U-Ringit puzzle. (R. Journet). (1950). (g). Sold August 2007: £8.10

▲ Speech Day puzzle (R. Journet). (1945). (g). Sold February 2008: £11.30

▲ The Queen Mary puzzle (R. Journet). (1935). (f). Sold September 2007: £10.10

▲ Royal National Lifeboat Institution puzzle. (1935). (f). Sold August 2007: £8.60

DIECAST MODELS

▲ Dinky Catalogue no.7.
1971. (vg). Sold
September 2010: £18.10

Some collectors will tell you that some of the most collectable diecast models are the airplanes, particularly those made before World War II. Some collectors will tell you to stick with cars, a popular subject that should result in the biggest number of interested buyers. Maybe models based on popular television shows such as Captain Scarlet, or commercial vehicles decorated in the livery of well-known companies, will generate the biggest sales? Everyone has an opinion.

There is, of course, certain things on which all collectors agree. Aim to buy quality, not quantity. Look for excellent or mint condition items with the original boxes to be in with a chance of selling at a good price, but don't be put off from buying play-worn items if the price is right. If you can pick up a well-loved car for £5 at a boot sale, and quickly sell it on for £10, then that's an investment which no small businessperson would sniff at!

Always try to avoid examples that have been repainted: A sloppy paint job looks horrible; a very good paint job makes the model seem like something it is not and may anger purchasers if they are not immediately aware that the paint is not original. Either way, if you are selling a model as repainted, the price you can expect to get is significantly reduced.

Collecting diecast models is not for the faint-hearted. Good condition examples can easily run to hundreds of pounds, and a serious collector must have deep pockets. Furthermore, if you have not taken the time to do your research, you may end up buying reproduction boxes or repainted and repaired models for sums far in excess of what they are actually worth. Make sure you read as much as you can on the subject area, and converse with experts.

▲ Vauxhall Victor (Matchbox). No box. 1958. (vg). Sold November 2010: £30.30

▲ Riley Pathfinder (Corgi). Original box. 1956-1961. (vg). Sold August 2010: £51.10

▲ Joe 90's car. 1969-1975. Repro box. (vg) Sold August 2010: £45.10

▲ Pullmore Car Transporter (Dinky). No box. 1955-1963. (vg). Sold November 2010: £32

▲ Bluebird Dauphine Caravan (Matchbox). 1960. (g). Sold March 2011: £6.20.

DISNEYANA

▲ Disneyland guide booklet. 1974. (g). Sold January 2010: £2

▲ Disneyland picture disc. 1977. (ex). Sold September 2009: £0.60

▲ Mickey Mouse candle. (1970). (vg). Sold February 2007: £5

▲ Disneyland Paris phonecard. 2005. (vg). Sold March 2010: £3.10

▲ Disney Moonwalk commemorative cover. 1980. (vg). Did not sell at £4 start price in January 2010.

▲ The Fox and the Hound DVD. 2000. (mnt). Sold November 2010: £8

DOCTOR WHO

The Doctors:	
1963 - 66	William Hartnell
1966 - 69	Patrick Troughton
1970 - 74	Jon Pertwee
1974 - 81	Tom Baker
1981 - 84	Peter Davison
1984 - 86	Colin Baker
1987 - 89 + 1996	Sylvester McCoy
1996	Paul McGann
2005	Chris Eccleston
2005 - 2010	David Tennant
2010 ⟶	Matt Smith

▲ Dr Who vinyl single. 1980. (vg). Sold October 2008: £10.10

▲ Dr Who signatures on commemorative cover. No dedications. Sold November 2009: £40.10

DOLLS

Dolls have been made all over the world, in all sizes, shapes and varieties. The choice is vast and though many dolls are very expensive, others are not; so there are many dolls available to suit all pockets.

It is important for a collector to have an understanding of materials as they can help in dating a doll. For example, dolls made from vinyl can't be much earlier than 1958 and could even be brand new, whereas dolls with porcelain heads can predate the Second World War and depending on style, body type and construction can be as early as 1870. It is very important to distinguish between old dolls made in France and Germany and originally sold in toy shops as playthings, and new bisque headed dolls which are made in China and sold in gift shops as ornaments.

Good quality wax dolls were made primarily, but not exclusively, in England in the nineteenth century and continued to be made as late as the 1920s. Unlike bisque headed dolls, they were not reproduced in large numbers, though some modern doll artists do still work with wax.

▲ German bisque headed doll. (1910). (g-vg). Sold June 2007: £90

Cloth dolls cannot be dated as a generic group as they have been made for centuries all over the world. But, as with most dolls, they can be dated very precisely by type, method of manufacture, and maker.

▲ Black Rosebud plastic doll. (1952). (vg). Sold June 2007: £25

Look out for dolls with all the original components with no damage, good colour, original wig and clothes and, if possible, box. Early dolls in this condition are obviously much harder to find.

Porcelain dolls (this includes those with glazed heads, those with only lightly tinted unglazed heads, and those with bisque heads) are greatly affected by the condition of the porcelain. A large chip or crack at the back of the head will reduce the price of the doll considerably and more unsightly damage will reduce it even more. From an investment point of view, don't buy damaged dolls. However, if your funds are limited and you like a damaged doll, it is very satisfying to restore it to its original condition.

▲ Pedigree vinyl doll. (1965). (vg-ex). Sold June 2007: £25

Whatever you decide to buy, be sure that you understand what you are buying, especially if a large price is involved. There are many pitfalls waiting to catch out the unwary. The best way to learn about dolls is to look at, and handle, as many of them as possible, and become familiar with all the many different methods of construction.

▲ Charlie Chaplin porcelain headed doll. (1971). (g). Sold November 2008: £7

EGG CUPS

▲ Sooty. (1960). (vg-ex). Sold March 2010: £20.10

▲ Dusty Bin. (1980). (vg). Sold November 2008: £12.60

▲ Smarties. 1987. (vg). Sold January 2010: £2.10

▲ Pink elephant. (1975). (g). Sold November 2008: £3.30

Collecting egg cups is known as pocillovy, and a collector is known as a pocillovist (pronounced po-sil-o-vist).

There is much more interest in the subject than you might at first realise. Novelty egg cups are particularly in demand; but, of course, egg cups shaped like chickens and other fowl are rather common.

Egg cups can often be picked up at relatively little expense, and it is easy to get a large collection; just remember that storage can become a problem, especially if you want your collection on display.

ELVIS

Elvis was a legend and an icon, adored by millions, and as a result this is an incredibly popular collecting subject.

There is an extraordinary amount of brand new Elvis merchandise still being produced every year. Because of the immense appeal of the subject matter, these items will be purchased in large quantities and therefore some of it will never be worth the huge sums of money that older, scarcer items will be worth. The lesson is to buy with caution.

▲ Blue Suede Shoes ceramic plate. 1999. (ex). Sold April 2010: £20.10

The best investments will usually be older items that many people will want but fewer people will actually already own, such as concert tickets, programmes, and advertising flyers. Vinyl records may seem like a safe bet, but in many cases Elvis records will not be worth too much due to the large quantities pressed when they were released. It is necessary to do some homework before investing heavily.

▲ In Tender Mood (EP). 1958. (vg). Sold July 2010: £15

▲ Peace in the Valley (EP). 1961. (g-vg). Sold February 2011: £7.20

▲ Meet Elvis (Elvis Monthly special). 1962. (vg-ex). Sold June 2010: £10

▲ Elvis 10 Years After festival flyer. 1987. (ex). Sold March 2010: £5.10

EPHEMERA

Ephemera generally refers to anything that was designed to be used and then thrown away, and as such it covers such a diverse range of items as railway tickets, postage stamps, theatre tickets and programmes, letters, telegrams, birthday cards, advertising, notices, and newspapers. Although ephemera items are normally considered to be paper, they can actually be made from any material.

Collecting ephemera has many benefits. Most of the time collections can be built at little expense as they will consist largely of items that other people are more than happy to discard after use. The sheer diversity of available ephemera means you are also able to tailor a collection to whatever your interest might be. For example, you may only want to collect train tickets or chocolate wrappers. Whatever your interest, there is bound to be some kind of ephemera related to it. In fact, because ephemera is such a general topic, it really is recommended that you collect to a theme, and the excitement of hunting down and finding an item can be quite a thrill.

Ephemera is something that is usually collected for the interesting nature of the items rather than for any investment potential; but that is not to say there is no investment potential at all. There is a healthy market at the moment for ephemera. And because ephemera is such a wide subject area you should always be able to find a few people who are interested in what you have to sell.

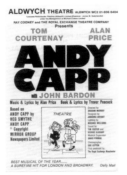

▲ Andy Capp musical flyer. 1981. (ex). Sold February 2011: £6

▲ Ford Motor Company warranty. 1914. (vg). Sold November 2010: £9.80

▲ Baggage labels. (1930). (g). Sold November 2010: £1.60

▲ Lined exercise book. (1965). (g-vg). Sold January 2011: £5.60

▲ National Lottery first draw ticket. 1994. (vg). Sold February 2011: £2

▲ Prize draw ticket. 1923. (g). Sold August 2010: £3.70

▲ Driving licence. 1926. (vg). Sold July 2010: £15

FILM POSTERS

▲ The Commitments. 1991. (g). Sold May 2009: £21

▲ Lucky Me. 1954. (vg). Sold July 2007: £23.70

▲ The Living Daylights. 1987. (vg). Sold May 2005: £52.50

▲ On the Run. 1958. (f-g). Sold May 2008: £15.10

FILM STRIPS

Film strips were popular with children in the 50s and 60s. They were also used for educational purposes, and many schools and colleges used them. They comprise still images that are projected onto a screen.

Film strips do not turn up that often at car boot sales, but can be found regularly on internet auction sites. Among the more collectable subjects is Nazi propaganda and classic comic characters such as Dan Dare.

▲ Jungle Terror. (1958). (vg). Sold January 2011: £8.10

▲ Adventures of Donald Duck. (1955). (f-g). Sold February 2009: £15.80

▲ Alibaba and the Forty Thieves. (1958). (vg). Sold January 2011: £5

▲ Laurel and Hardy. (1955). (g). Sold June 2007: £13.50

▲ Dan Dare. (1960). (vg). Sold January 2011: £18.70

FIRST DAY COVERS

A First Day Cover is an envelope or card (often specially designed) with newly issued postage stamps that were postmarked on the first day of issue. They date from 6 May 1840, when the first national postage stamps were issued for use (the Penny Black and Twopenny Blue); however, there were no "official" First Day Covers until the 1960s.

In essence, a First Day Cover consists of three specific elements: the cover (envelope or card), the postmarks (sometimes referred to as cancellations or franks), and the stamps.

In order to be a worthy collector's piece, all three elements of the First Day Cover should be related.

▲ Definitives. 15 Feb 1971. (g). Sold February 2011: £5

▲ Speed. 13 Oct 1998. (ex). Sold November 2010: £4.10

▲ Westminster Abbey. 28 Feb 1966. (vg). Sold March 2010: £8

▲ Horse Racing. 6 Jun 1979. (vg). Sold March 2009: £10.10

▲ County Cricket Centenary. 16 May 1973. (vg). Sold May 2010: £4.10

▲ British Landscapes. 2 May 1966. (g). Sold March 2010: £10.10

▲ British Bridges. 29 Apr 1968. (vg). Sold March 2009: £8

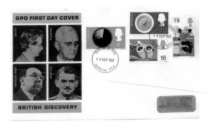

▲ British Discovery. 19 Sep 1967. (vg). Sold January 2010: £5

FOOTBALL

▲ FA Hall of Fame commemorative cover. 1970. (ex). Sold August 2010: £6.10

▲ Chelsea v Tottenham Hotspur FA Cup Final commemorative cover. 1967. (vg). Sold February 2010: £6.10

▲ Leeds United commemorative cover. 1992. (ex). Sold January 2010: £9.30

▲ Arsenal champion rosette. 1971. (g). Sold June 2010: £20.10

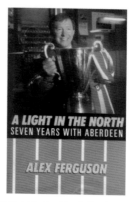

▲ A Light in the North (book). 1985. (vg). Sold August 2010: £20.10

▲ European Cup metal pin badge. 1979. (vg). Sold August 2010: £8.20

▲ Teddy Sheringham phonecard. 1996. (ex). Sold February 2010: £4.10

▲ Tottenham Hotspur pencil case. (1990). (g). Sold June 2010: £0.60

▲ England embroidered cloth badge. (1975). (g). Sold January 2010: £4.10

▲ We Will Stand Together (Manchester Utd vinyl single). 1990. (ex). Sold June 2010: £3.80

▲ Sports Argus Football Annual. 1951. (p). Sold November 2009: £10

▲ Arsenal official handbook. 1955. (f-g). Sold January 2010: £4.10

FOOTBALL PROGRAMMES

The first football programmes were produced in the 1870s. They were extremely basic (usually a single sheet) and were used to enable fans to identify the players and to notify them of forthcoming features.

In the 1900s, football clubs began to realise that a profit could be made from programmes and cover prices began to rise. The quality also improved, so the programmes were no longer single sheets and began to resemble the programmes we see today. By the 1920s, programmes were used by the majority of clubs, and they were very popular.

The quality of football programmes suffered a major setback due to paper rationing after World War II, but in 1966 the World Cup increased the nation's interest in football, and programmes were completely modernised. By the 1970s, many programmes were using glossy paper, and had begun to resemble magazines.

▲ Charlton Athletic v Bolton Wanderers. 24 Apr 1937. (g-vg). Sold January 2010: £70

▲ Chelsea v Blackburn Rovers. 4 Apr 1947. (f-g). Sold March 2011: £25.10

▲ Aston Villa Reserves v Wrexham. April 1907. (g). Sold April 2010: £100

▲ Ireland v England. 22 Oct 1966. (g-vg). Sold March 2011: £10.10

▲ Portsmouth v Wolverhampton Wanderers. 16 Apr 1949. (g). Sold March 2011: £22.10

▲ Upminster v Leyton. 9 Oct 1948. (vg). Sold March 2011: £10.10

▲ Arsenal v Portsmouth. 25 Dec 1946. (g-vg). Sold January 2011: £20.30

▲ West Ham United v Cardiff City. 3 Dec 1960. (vg). Sold February 2011: £12.10

▲ Manchester United v Manchester City. 23 Sep 1961. (vg). Sold March 2011: £10

▲ Cowdenbeath v St Johnstone. 22 August 1953. (f-g). Sold February 2011: £15.10

▲ Queens Park v Ayr United. 31 Oct 1953. (vg). Sold November 2010: £30.10

▲ Arsenal v Ipswich Town FA Cup Final. 6 May 1978. (g). Sold September 2010: £25.10

▲ Maidenhead United v Grays Athletic. 15 Sep 1945. (g). Sold August 2010: £25.10

▲ Derby County v Sunderland. 11 Sep 1948. (vg). Sold March 2010: £30.10

▲ Birmingham City v Blackpool FA Challenge Cup Semi-Final. 10 Mar 1951. (vg). Sold March 2010: £90.10

GAMES

The condition of a board game, as with all collectables, is vitally important; but unlike other collectables, there are lots of different "bits" to consider with a game.

A lot of game collectors actually like to play with their collection, so a game should be complete and playable. There should be instructions, dice, counters, the board, etc. All of these different elements should be nice and clean. One missing dice is not the end of the world, as it is easy enough to find a replacement that looks the same as the original, but complete sets that do not require restoration of any kind are the best bet for a sound investment. You should also pay particular attention to the box, which is often as important as what is inside. The cover image should be clean and bright, with no stains. It is common for boxed games to be stacked on top of each other, and this can cause box lids to "cave in", as well as ripping the corners. Boxes that have been repaired poorly with sticky tape are not likely to be a big hit with collectors unless the contents are in exceptional condition, or the game is a particularly rare one that is hard to find in good condition.

Losing the playing pieces for a game is one of the easiest ways of devaluing it. Some games come with plastic box inserts that allow cards and counters to be separated out and safely stored, but other games don't. If you want to make sure you have all the "bits", invest in some small sealable plastic bags. Use a different bag for each type of counter or playing piece, and label the bags accordingly (for example, "ten red counters" or "200 card tokens"). This will also help when selling the game, as a potential buyer will immediately be able to see that all the playing pieces are present and correct.

▲ Tail-less Donkey. (1925). (g). Sold February 2011: £15

▲ Blow football. (1955). (vg). Sold November 2010: £28.10

▲ Z-Cars board game. (1965). (vg). Sold January 2010: £16.10

▲ Tufty Road Safety board game. (1968). (vg). Sold January 2010: £3.00

▲ Totopoly game. 1949. (vg). Sold May 2010: £25.10

▲ Kojak board game. 1975. (vg). Sold April 2008: £10

GOLLIES

▲ Golly enamel badge. (1965). (g-vg). Sold April 2008: £35.10

The golly has a strong association with James Robertson and Sons, who began using the character for promotional purposes in the early 1900s. He remained the company mascot and logo until being dropped in 2001.

The "golly" was part of many promotions where coupons could be exchanged for a badge. One enamel badge was exchanged for ten paper golly tokens, which could be found affixed behind each jar label. The paper gollies were a variety of musicians and sportsmen, and the 60s and 70s varieties of these are becoming more collectable. Now could be the time to start building a collection while prices are still relatively low. As with all collectable items, condition plays an important role in the item's value.

The earlier enamel badges (pre-1960) are the more valuable and most collectable. However, there are plenty of fakes (and official reproductions). Therefore, it is important not to buy until you know exactly what you are looking for (there are plenty of websites with specialist information). Pay particular attention to backstamps to identify the age and authenticity.

▲ Golly plaster model. (1980). (g). Sold June 2008: £4.10

▲ Golden Shred Ford Van Lledo diecast model. 1988. (mnt). Sold June 2008: £19

▲ Golly paper coupon. (1965). (vg). Sold 23 May 2006: £2.60

▲ Golden Shred Preston Tramcar Matchbox diecast model. 1986. (ex). Sold March 2010: £40.30

GRAMOPHONE NEEDLE TINS

Collecting gramophones not only requires a lot of money, they take up a lot of space. A great alternative is gramophone needles which were supplied in attractive little tins.

Gramophone needles are not immediately identifiable as a collecting area until you delve into the subject matter. Every time a 78rpm record was played, a new needle had to be used. Gramophones were hugely popular between 1920 and 1950, and records were sold by the million. There were plenty of companies producing gramophone needles and they were generally sold in attractively designed little tins which are now a joy to collect.

The most common tins are HMV, but other notable names are Decca, Songster, Columbia, and Embassy. Needles were also sold in packets and boxes.

▲ HMV. (1935). (vg). Sold November 2010: £15.10

▲ Embassy. (1925). (f-g). Sold February 2009: £15

▲ Songster. (1930). (f). Sold February 2009: £10.10

▲ Columbia. (1940). (g). Sold May 2008: £7.60

▲ Decca. (1940). (vg). Sold February 2008: £14

▲ Edison Bell. (1930). (g). Sold May 2008: £16.60

▲ HMV. (1930). (f). Sold February 2009: £14

▲ Rex. (1925). (g). Sold February 2008: £16.10

▲ Parrot. (1940). (g). Sold October 2006: £10.10

GREETINGS CARDS

Boxes of old greetings cards can turn up at boot sales or can be sold as collections on internet auctions. An entire box can often be purchased for next to nothing and you just may find a real gem or two hidden inside.

Collecting greetings cards can be a social history study, with the images reflecting fashion and lifestyle. Early valentine cards (pre-1900) can command decent sums. The subject is so wide that collectors often concentrate on a specific topic such as wedding day cards or Easter cards.

There's lots of information available on the subject via internet search engines, and it doesn't take long to acquire enough knowledge to become quite an expert.

Look out for specially printed cards for serving members of the armed forces. Messages can be interesting and value is added when there's a regimental badge or other image (for example a Royal Navy ship).

▲ Mabel Lucie Atwell birthday card. (1950). (vg). Sold September 2010: £3.30

From 1900 to 1939 greetings cards in the form of postcards were extremely popular, while children's pop-up cards from the 40s and 50s often have charming artwork and are not overly expensive. Celebrated artists, such as Mabel Lucie Attwell, are also desirable.

▲ Christmas Greetings (Middle East Forces) card. 1944. (vg). Sold January 2011: £12.40

▲ Lest We Forget card. (1915). (vg). Sold September 2010: £4.90

▲ "You auto have a dandy trip" card. (1930). (vg). Sold September 2010: £3.20

▲ Pop-up card. 1956. (vg). Sold September 2010: £8.10

▲ Christmas greetings silk card. (1915). (vg). Sold September 2010: £6.10

▲ May joy fly to you. (1920). (vg). Sold September 2010: £0.70

GREYHOUND RACING

Despite not being as popular as horseracing, 'the dogs' still have a sizable following and therefore a market exists for collectables. Look out for old programmes and race cards, betting tickets, badges, official documents, and postcards (particularly those for stadiums that no longer exist).

Items relating to the most famous greyhounds command a premium. Arguably, the most famous greyhound of all time is Mick the Miller (born 1926) although supporters of Ballyregan Bob (born 1986) may disagree.

The best searching ground for items is the internet. The larger stadiums may attract the odd memorabilia stall holder; however, the large horseracing course regular vendors of books and other items will quite often include greyhound items on their stalls.

▲ Walthamstow Stadium matchbook. (1980). (vg). Sold April 2011: £3.60

▲ Clapton Stadium (greyhound) owner's pass. 1973. (g) Sold April 2011: £1

GUINNESS

▲ Toucan enamel pin badge. (1995). (ex). Sold March 2010: £10.10

▲ Guinness bottle tops. (1970). (vg). Sold 19 February 2008: £1.00

Guinness now has an iconic status, meaning any item branded with the Guinness logo (especially unusual items) will prove popular with collectors. Look out for good examples where the famous harp is nice and clear.

Old advertisments featuring the artwork of John Gilroy are also a big draw for collectors.

▲ Guinness glass goblet. 2000. (ex). Sold 13 May 2008: £30.00

▲ Ceramic money box. (2005). (ex). Sold November 2008: £10

▲ Salt cellar. (1990). (vg). Sold November 2008: £12.50

HORSE RACING

▲ The Sporting Life beer mat. (1960). (vg). Sold February 2011: £6.40

▲ Derby Winner drinking set. (1960). (g-vg). Sold February 2008: £24.40

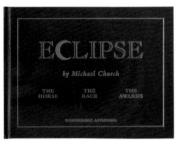

▲ Eclipse (book). 2000. (ex). Sold April 2011: £30.60

▲ Newmarket enamel badge. 1979. (vg-ex). Sold March 2011: £6.90

▲ Ascot card badge. 1993. (vg). Sold March 2011: £1.20

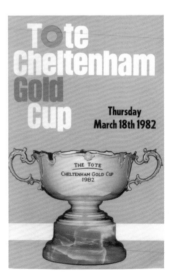

▲ York racecard. 19 August 1969. (g). Sold April 2011: £2.60

▲ Warwick racecard. 29 April 1968. (ex). Sold April 2011: £2

▲ Towcester racecard. 20 April 1981. (vg-ex). Sold April 2011: £1

▲ Kempton racecard. 12 May 1951. (g). Sold April 2011: £3

▲ Beverley racecard. 24 May 1952. (vg) Sold April 2011: £4.60

▲ Towcester racecard. 12 April 1982. (ex). Sold April 2011: £1

▲ Cheltenham Gold Cup race card. 1982. (vg-ex). Sold April 2011: £4

I-SPY

The I-SPY Tribe had, at its head, Big Chief I-SPY. Founded originally by the long defunct News Chronicle, the tribe had been hugely successful at its peak in the 1950s and early 60s, but as children came under the influence of television its popularity waned.

The idea behind I-Spy books was that as the children found various items, they would tick them off in the book, and perhaps write a brief note about where they saw the items and what they were used for. This means that many of the I-Spy books you are likely to find at car boot sales and similar places will have writing on at least some of the pages (if not all of them). It goes without saying that unused, clean examples will demand a premium among collectors.

▲ I-Spy Tribe button badge. 1958. (g-vg). Sold August 2009: £7.60

▲ Boats & Waterways. (1963). (g). Sold March 2010: £4.20

▲ Pets. (1968). (g). Sold March 2010: £2

▲ Town Crafts. (1958). (g-vg). Sold June 2009: £1.20

▲ Everyday Machines. 1958. (vg). Sold June 2009: £2

▲ Bridges. 1958. (g-vg). Sold February 2009: £5

▲ The Land. 1958. (g-vg).Sold February 2009: £6.50

JAMES BOND

▲ Playing cards. 2001. (vg). Sold May 2008: £7.50

▲ BMW 750i Corgi diecast model. 2006. (ex-mnt). Sold February 2011: £10.10

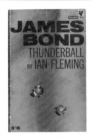

▲ Thunderball (paperback book). 1963. (f). Sold June 2010: £3.10

▲ James Bond Greatest Hits vinyl LP. 1982. (vg). Sold August 2009: £2.10

▲ Jaguar XKR Corgi diecast model. 2007. (ex-mnt). Sold February 2011: £10.10

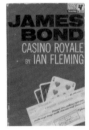

▲ Casino Royale (paperback book). 1965. (f). Sold June 2010: £3.10

JAZZ

This is one of those subjects that has a niche following and therefore has a niche market. Buying interesting jazz items is relatively simple. The secret is to sell to the right audience and therefore you could consider advertising in specialist jazz magazines or on enthusiast websites.

Old jazz magazines are tremendous (look for pre-1950). Legendary musicians are often featured with photographs, increasing the value. Jazz records can also have value, although this is dangerous ground unless you have done your homework properly.

▲ Jazz Music magazine. 1947. (g). Sold September 2010: £3.50

Original sheet music is quite collectable. As well as the obvious musical score, a photograph of the artist on the front cover adds to the interest. However, jazz sheet music is generally not as desirable as 60s pop.

Books are also worth considering. Autobiographies of the legends are in demand, particularly pre-1960.

Autographs, especially ones on publicity photographs without a dedication, are in demand. Concert programmes and tickets are also highly sought after. Add autographs to concert programmes and you could have some serious items on your hands.

▲ Django Reinhardt vinyl LP. (1960). (vg). Sold September 2010: £5.30

KEY RINGS

▲ South Park keyrings. (2000). (ex). Sold June 2007: £10

▲ Butlin's photo viewer keyring. (1970). (vg). Sold April 2008: £15

▲ Esso Man keyring. (1960). (vg-ex).Sold November 2008: £35.10

▲ Coronation Street keyring. (1990). (g). Sold June 2010: £2.50

▲ Joe Cool (Snoopy) keyring. (1980). (g). Sold December 2008: £3.60

KEYS

▲ Iron key. (1875). 60mm long. (g). Sold May 2008: £7.70

▲ Lever key. (1900). 60mm long. (vg). Sold February 2005: £1.90

▲ Old key. (1915). 115mm long. (g). Sold May 2006: £1

▲ Milner's safe key. (1910). 75mm long. (g). Sold February 2005: £1.50

▲ RAF door key. (1945). 110mm long. (f-g). Sold March 2008: £11.51

▲ Door key. (1850). 137mm long. (vg). Sold May 2008: £20

▲ Old key. (1900). 105mm long. (g). Sold February 2005: £3.60

KITCHENALIA

▲ Aluminium éclair moulds. (1960). (ex). Sold October 2005: £8.70

▲ Spong mincer. (1955). (f). Sold August 2007: £10

▲ Tala cream horn moulds. (1950). (vg). Sold October 2005: £8.10

▲ De Ve coffee grinder. (1975). (g). Sold August 2005: £9

▲ Tala icing set. (1950). (vg). Sold January 2007: £10.10

▲ Spong bean slicer. (1950). (g). Sold February 2005: £2

▲ Tala towel holder. (1965). (ex). Sold October 2005: £15.10

▲ Rotary tabletop knife sharpener. (1960). (g-vg). Sold August 2005: £3.20

▲ Universal mincer. (1960). Sold August 2007: £6.

▲ Marmalade cutter. (1935). (g). Sold March 2008: £9.20

LADYBIRD BOOKS

The first Ladybird book, "Bunnikin's Picnic Party," was produced by Wills & Hepworth in 1940.

It can be quite difficult to date Ladybird books accurately and harder still to establish if you have a first edition. Between 1940 and 1965 Ladybird books were produced with dust jackets, and in the back there was a list of other books in that particular series. If the name of the book you are reading appears anywhere in the list OTHER THAN the very bottom, then the book you have will not be a first edition. However, please be advised that if the name of the book is last on the list, or does not appear at all, this is not a guarantee that the book is a first edition, and it will be necessary for you to do further research to verify the date.

Over the years Ladybird Books have carried several different logos, and these can be used to help date any of the books you have in your collection. Up until 1961, the logo was an openwinged ladybird. This design was then changed to a ladybird with closed wings. In 1965 the design was changed again; the ladybird still had closed wings, but was now in colour, surrounded by a black box, and was usually found in the top right or bottom right corner of the front cover. Other designs were introduced in the 1970s and 1980s, but it is the 1965 logo that is most commonly recognised.

▲ People at Work: The Fireman. 1962. (g). Sold February 2009: £4.10

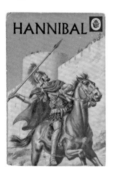
▲ Hannibal. 1974. (g). Sold February 2009: £6.20

▲ Tricks and Magic. 1969. (g). Sold November 2008: £7.10

▲ London. 1965. (vg). Sold June 2008: £6

LIGHTERS

▲ Player's Gold Leaf. (1970). (vg). Sold March 2010: £12.20

▲ Camel table lighter. (1900). 109mm tall. (vg). Sold May 2009: £51

▲ Ronson table lighter. (1970). (g-vg). Sold February 2009: £8.70

▲ Ronson Whirlwind. (1955). (vg). Sold February 2009: £6.90

MAGAZINES

There are a few things to look out for when trying to establish if a magazine has any value. You should preferably be looking for some, or all, of the following characteristics: Good condition (or better), rare, a first or last ever issue, good cover art (or photograph), and some interesting content such as the first printing of a famous story or an article on a celebrity.

▲ Punch. 1954. (g-vg). Sold February 2011: £5.10

▲ Boyfriend's Startime Extra. 1964. (vg). Sold February 2011: £15.90

▲ Look-in. 1973. (vg). Sold February 2011: £11.30

▲ The Motor Cycle. 1939. (f). Sold January 2011: £12.10

▲ Transatlantic Film Star Parade. (1950). (vg). Sold August 2010: £6.60

▲ The Geographical Magazine. 1961. (vg). Sold March 2010: £2.10

▲ Wide World. 1961. (g-vg). Sold June 2009: £5.10

▲ The Ring. 1952. (f). Sold February 2011: £3.

▲ Woman's Weekly. 1966. (f). Sold June 2011: £0.50

▲ Practical Mechanics. 1958. (vg). Sold June 2009: £4.80

▲ Practical Television. 1966. (vg). Sold January 2011: £2

▲ Practical Householder. 1958. (g). Sold February 2008: £7

▲ Weekly Film News. 1949. (vg-ex). Sold June 2010: £4.50

▲ The Oil & Colour Trades Journal. 1912. (g). Sold June 2010: £6.50

▲ St George's Magazine for Boys and Girls. 1910. (vg). Sold May 2010: £6.10

▲ Lilliput. 1944. (vg). Sold May 2010: £2.60

MAGIC LANTERNS

The Magic Lantern was the forerunner of the movies. Still images were transferred to glass slides and projected to a screen or wall. They had reached the height of their popularity in the early part of the 20th century. While the projectors are not in plentiful supply, the slides are not too difficult to find, although many of them may be missing some paint due to age and wear.

▲ Butterflies. (1890). (f). Sold April 2008: £6.10

▲ Children's band. (1910). (g-vg). Did not sell at £3 start price in March 2011.

▲ Boating. (1910). (g). Sold February 2009: £6.10

MAPS & GUIDES

▲ Road map. 1950. (g). Sold November 2010: £2.10

▲ Motorists' road map of England. (1920). (g). Sold April 2010: £5.20

▲ London Underground railway map. 1938. (g). Sold January 2010: £8.20

▲ Map & street directory of Crosby. (1950). (f). Sold March 2009: £4.50

▲ England and Wales road map. (1925). (g). Sold April 2008: £5.90

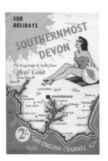

▲ Southernmost Devon guide. 1957. (g). Sold February 2008: £3.10

▲ Motoring and Seeing Old Railways in Devon. (1960). (vg). Sold November 2010: £5.20

▲ Motoring in Britain. (1950). (vg). Sold March 2010: £5.10

MATCHBOOKS

The first matchbook (matches affixed to a small card cover with a striking device) appeared around 1890. The potential for advertisements to be placed on matchbooks was soon realised. Collectors are mainly interested in pre-1950 and/or specialist themes. For example, old airlines/shipping/motoring. Look out for job lots on internet auction websites or at car boot sales. While the bulk may be virtually worthless, a few could be seriously collectable.

▲ Pan Am. (1975). (g). Sold March 2010: £2.10

▲ Bristol cigarettes. (1960). (g-vg). Sold December 2008: £3.20

▲ Edgar Allen & Co. (1955). (vg). Sold September 2009: £6.90

▲ Dr Barnarddo's Homes. (1955). Sold September 2009: £3.50

▲ Curzon. (1955). (vg). Sold September 2009: £6.90

MATCHBOXES & MATCHBOX LABELS

In 1833, the German J Kammerer began manufacturing phosphorous matches on an industrial basis. Around the same time, wax matches were invented. The matches were originally sold in bundles, but were subsequently sold in boxes, many with decorative labels. As well as matchboxes, some people will also collect matchbox labels.

▲ Moscow 80 (Olympics). 1984. (g). Sold June 2008: £0.30

▲ Butlin's. (1965). (g). Sold March 2011: £4.90.

▲ Silver Jubilee. 1977. (g). Sold May 2008: £1.20.

▲ The Blue Cross. (1965). (f-g). Sold May 2008: £1.10.

▲ Punch. (1975). (vg). Sold May 2008: £0.30.

▲ Co-op. (1975). (f). Sold September 2008: £0.60.

▲ Locomotive. (1955). (f). Sold November 2010: £3.60

▲ Los Angeles 84 (Olympics). 1984. (g). Sold June 2008: £0.30.

McDONALD'S TOYS

Since 1977 (1984 in the UK), fast food chain McDonald's has been issuing free toys with Happy Meals. These premiums helped to increase the sales of burgers and fries, but they also had a rather unexpected side-effect. The popular themes and characters of the toys, and the low cost associated with acquiring them, meant they soon became popular collectables, and there are now collectors all over the world trying to complete their sets.

▲ Snoopy. 1999. (g). Sold December 2008: £1.60

▲ Smurf. 1996. (g). Sold December 2008: £2.60

As with other toys such as Dinky and Matchbox models, McDonalds premiums were designed to be played with, and they often didn't survive for long in the hands of the children they were made for. This means that some of the early examples can be very hard to find, and as surprising as it may seem, these free toys are actually starting to fetch good prices at sales and online auctions.

The first thing to realise is that this is a massive collecting area. New premiums are issued by the restaurant chain every few weeks, so you can really be kept on your toes just keeping up-to-date. For example, in a Disney's 101 Dalmatians promotion, there were 101 different toy dogs to collect. That's certainly a lot of burgers to chomp through to get them all, and even more pain-staking effort seeking them all out on the secondary market.

It is also worth noting that premiums are different depending on the country, so there are regional variations and country-specific items to watch out for as well, making it almost impossible to collect every premium available. Collectors are strongly advised to collect to specific themes to save on headaches!

Many people forget that the Happy Meal boxes, in which the meal and toy arrives, can be collectable too. All too often the boxes will be thrown away, making the surviving boxes very difficult to find, and therefore more valuable.

The most desirable toys are the ones that wind up or have moving parts – the same toys that are most likely to have broken if they were played with rather than carefully stored or displayed.

▲ Sully (light up). 2004. (vg). Sold April 2008: £1

▲ Beeker plush. 2004. (ex). Sold December 2006: £2.10

Finally, always buy in bulk if possible, when going around boot sales and the like, as you will probably get a much better deal than if you just buy one or two toys at a time.

MECCANO

Meccano was invented by Frank Hornby in 1901. It was originally called 'Mechanics Made Easy', but the name was changed in 1907. Hornby would go on to invent other classic toys such as Hornby Model Railways and Dinky Toys.

There's good money to be made from dabbling in the Meccano collectors' market. However, this is a classic case of having to do your homework before getting too heavily involved.

Serious collectors look for full sets in original boxes with all of the original parts, but there are also plenty of less-serious collectors around who are not so picky

▲ Accessory Outfit no. 4A instruction booklet. 1957. (f). Sold February 2009: £5.20

and enthusiastically look for the right parts to build particular models. There are lots of reproduction parts on the market that may satisfy this type of collector, but those looking to buy genuine parts should check that everything they are buying is stamped with the Meccano name.

Standard pieces such as perforated strips, angle brackets, rods, and pulley wheels can often be found at car boot sales and can be bought loose for pennies.

Look out for unusual parts such as railway signals, ships' funnels, and compass needles. These tend to be harder to find and will therefore command a premium among collectors.

The more valuable Meccano sets can be found at auctions and should be examined before buying.

Collectors also look out for Meccano instruction booklets, empty boxes, and copies of old editions of Meccano Magazine. All of these things have a habit of turning up at car boot sales and collectors' fairs. Buy at the right prices and there is lots of potential for good profit.

▲ Meccano magazine. 1958. (vg).Sold March 2011: £5.20

▲ Ten green strips. (1965). (g). Sold February 2009: £2.40

▲ Meccano spanner. (1965). (g). Sold February 2009: £1.60

▲ Accessory Outfit empty box. (1950). (g-vg). Sold November 2010: £8

▲ Meccano Outfit no. 5 instruction booklet. (1960). (f). Sold September 2007: £12.10

MEDALS (MILITARY)

▲ The France and Germany Star. 1944-1945. (ex). Sold February 2009: £24.50

▲ Atlantic Star. 1939-1945. (vg). Sold February 2009: £30.20

▲ Liberation of Kuwait. 1991. (ex). Sold July 2010: £20.10

▲ United Nations Protection Force. 1992-1996. (ex). Sold November 2008: £20.10

▲ Republic of Vietnam service medal. 1965-1973. (ex).Sold September 2008: £25.10

▲ WWII Star. 1939-1945. (g-vg). Sold May 2008: £15.10

▲ The Burma Star (no ribbon). 1941-1945. (g). Sold April 2008: £15.20

▲ Air Medal. 1939-present. (ex). Sold April 2008: £20

▲ Belgian Prisoner of War Medal. 1940-1945. (ex). Sold March 2008: £25.01

▲ The Defence Medal. 1939-1945. (ex). Sold March 2008: £17.50

▲ Purple Heart. 1917-present. (ex). Sold February 2008: £50.10

▲ George VI Imperial Service Medal. 1936-1952. (ex). Sold September 2007: £45.10

MILITARIA

Militaria is a broad collecting area that comprises anything relating to the Armed Forces, as such it encapsulates other collecting areas such as medals, aeronautica, nauticalia, postcards, and much more.

▲ The War Illustrated paper. 1940. (vg). Sold March 2011: £5.20

▲ Sheet of 25 Hitler stamps. 1942. (mnt). Sold March 2011: £40.40

▲ 30 reproduction plastic regimental badges (Texaco promotion). (1970). (vg). Sold February 2011: £21

One area of militaria that can provide hours of pleasure is collecting cap badges. The intricate designs are heraldic symbols and it is fascinating researching their meanings.

◀ 19th PWO Hussars cap badge. (1900). (vg). Sold February 2011: £21.90

There are hundreds of variations. Watch out for subdued or blackened versions: These were worn on the battlefield because shiny brass versions might have attracted the attention of enemy soldiers.

◀ Glider Regiment Pilot cap badge. 1957. (vg). Sold February 2011: £20.10

A good tip is to visit a few Collectors' Fairs and tax brains of the stall holders. Most large fairs often have two or three specialists selling army cap badges. Look at the prices being asked and learn how to spot fakes (there are plenty around, particularly on the internet).

▲ The Battle of Britain (booklet). 1941. (g). Sold November 2010: £15.10

▲ Recruiting post-card. 1917. (g-vg). Sold August 2010: £7.20

▲ Princess Mary Christmas gift tin. 1914. (vg). Sold March 2010: £30.10

▲ Adjutant British 54th Infantry model soldier. (2000). (f). Sold July 2010: £5.10

MILK BOTTLES

The interest in collecting milk bottles really took off in the early '80s when many dairies printed advertisements on their bottles. This was not a new concept, but one that had never really been exploited properly.

Generally, advertising on milk bottles ceased in the early '90s because the scanning equipment used for making hygiene checks was impaired by the images.

Bottles need to be undamaged and in good condition or better. Some advertisements are more interesting than others. For example, a South Wales Police advertisement is far more collectable than a general advertisement for orange juice. The police advert would also appeal to collectors of police memorabilia and would therefore have a larger market as well.

Pre-1950 bottles with the names of dairies are also collectable.

Collectable milk bottles have a habit of turning up at car boot sales and are often dismissed as worthless. A downside to collecting and trading them is the space they take up and the cost of postage and packing.

▲ Breakfast with Bowyers. (1988). (g). Sold February 2011: £1

▲ The Mirror. 1986. (g). Sold February 2011: £3

▲ LBC Radio. (1990). (g). Sold February 2011: £3

▲ Knorr. (1988). (g). Sold February 2011: £2

▲ Twix. (1990). (g). Sold February 2011: £3

▲ Mars. (1990). (g). Sold February 2011: £3

▲ Horlicks. (1988). (vg). Sold March 2011: £5.10

▲ Pure Fruit Juice. (1987). (vg). Sold March 2011: £4.10

▲ Brooke Bond D. (1985). (g). Sold June 2009: £4.10

▲ Ready Brek. (1985). (vg). Sold June 2009: £4.10

MODEL RAILWAY

▲ Hornby rail freight set. 1977. (vg). Sold March 2011: £20.70

▲ Tri-ang Hornby catalogue. 1971. (vg). Sold November 2010: £15.30

▲ Hornby 501 clockwork train set. (1948). (vg). Sold September 2010: £100.10

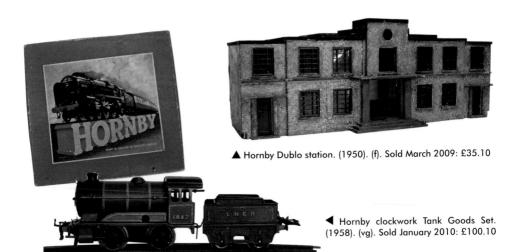

▲ Hornby Dublo station. (1950). (f). Sold March 2009: £35.10

◄ Hornby clockwork Tank Goods Set. (1958). (vg). Sold January 2010: £100.10

MONEY BOXES

Money boxes can be fun and colourful collectables, but be warned that they can quickly take up quite a lot of space, and if you are intending to sell them via post then you may need to ensure they are very carefully wrapped to avoid any damage.

One of the most popular series of money boxes is the Natwest pigs. Wade pottery produced the series in 1983 (taking over from Sunshine Ceramics who originally made the pigs in 1982). The idea was to give youngsters an incentive to save. As a child's balance grew, they were able to increase their collection of pigs. More on these money boxes can be found under "Wade" later in this book.

▲ Snoopy. (1970). (g-vg). Sold March 2008: £10.10

▲ VW Camper Van. (1995). (g). Sold July 2008: £10

▲ M&M's. 2001. (vg). Sold November 2008: £8

▲ Oxo (Coronation souvenir). 1937. (g-vg). Sold May 2009: £25

▲ Lloyds bank. (1975). (g). Sold November 2009: £7

▲ Garfield. (1980). (vg). Sold February 2009: £12.10

MOTOR RACING

Motor racing is a sub-category of automobilia. Items to watch out for in this category include race day programmes and signed memorabilia.

▲ Motor Racing Tom Thumb cigarette cards. 1989. (ex). Sold August 2010: £10.10

▲ Nigel Mansell postcard.1989. (ex). Sold November 2007: £2.10

▲ Goodwood programme. 1956. (g). Sold February 2008: £4.30

▲ Stirling Moss autographed picture. Dedicated. Sold March 2011: £12.10

◄ Monaco baseball cap. 1997. (ex). Sold November 2005: £8.10

▲ Maserati racing car Dinky model. 1954-1960. (f-g). Sold November 2010: £28.10

MOTOR CYCLING

▲ Supersport 600 Series phonecard. 1999. (mnt). Sold January 2011: £12

► Michelin sticker. (1980). (ex). Sold January 2011: £0.90

▲ Motor Cycling with Scooter Weekly. 1962. (g). Sold June 2009: £6.80

▲ BSA pin badge. (1985). (vg).Sold January 2006: £6.70

MOVIES (8mm)

This category of collectables appeals to both enthusiasts who view these films using 8mm film projectors and general movie enthusiasts. For example, Stagecoach starring John Wayne was released on 8mm and just the box is a collectable item (although the film is obviously of greater value). Watch out though: You do need to check that the correct film is in the correct box (hold the first few feet of film up to a bright light to check). The best source for these is internet auctions.

Some events, such as the Apollo Moon Landing and the World Cup 1966 are particularly collectable. The Beatles – A Hard Day's Night (with sound) is also a strong collectable.

▲ Fight Night (Keystone Comedy). (1945). (vg). Did not sell at £10 start price in November 2010.

▲ Safety Spin (Mr Magoo). (1972). (vg). Did not sell at £4 start price in November 2010.

▲ Apollo 12 On the Moon. 1970. (vg). Sold November 2010: £12

▲ Pluto – First Aiders (1965). (g). Sold November 2010: £3

NODDY

On 11 August 1897, in East Dulwich, Enid Mary Blyton was born; less than two months later, in a different country, Harmsen van der Beek was born. Who could have known then, that these two people would join forces to create one of the most enduring characters in children's literature?

It seemed that Enid Blyton was always destined to be a writer. One of her favourite pastimes was reading, and she was writing her own short stories and poetry from a very early age. Her first book, a collection of poems entitled Child Whispers, was published in 1922. It is a book that is now desperately sought by Enid Blyton collectors all over the world.

Her first book was just a taste of things to come, and she went on to have an incredibly successful career. It seems surprising that it was not until 1949, after many years of writing that she hit upon the idea of Noddy. Dutch illustrator Harmsen van der Beek provided the illustrations and his artwork was so beautiful, full of character and colour, that he was as much responsible for Noddy's success as Enid Blyton was. Enid Blyton herself is known to have said that van der Beek drew Noddy just as she had imagined him to be.

▲ Noddy postcard. (1965). (vg-ex). Sold November 2010: £15.10

Unfortunately, van der Beek passed away in 1953 (the year book seven in the Noddy Library was published by Sampson Low), so all subsequent adventures were drawn by other illustrators, although the style was kept consistent.

▲ Noddy and The Three Bears. 1952. (f-g). Sold February 2008: £16

▲ Noddy pin badge. (1965). (g). Sold May 2008: £6

NUMISMATICS

Numismatics is the study and collection of coins.

If you embark on such a hobby it is important to remember that being frequently handled or exposed to air will cause coins to discolour. Furthermore, you should never polish coins, as this can leave tiny scratches on the surface that will devalue them.

(Front) (Obverse) (Reverse)

▲ Uncirculated £2 coin. 1986. (ex). Sold January 2010: £16

(Cover) (Inside)

▲ Uncirculated coin collection. 1988. (mnt). Sold January 2010: £15.10

OBSERVER'S BOOKS

The first two titles in Frederick Warne & Co's popular series of Observer's books, British Birds and British Wild Flowers, were published in 1937, and their popularity led to the series expanding dramatically. Eventually there were 97 titles in the series, spanning everything from Cathedrals to Football.

The last book was number 98, Opera, published in 1982. That may seem strange, considering there were only 97 books in the series, but number 86, Country Houses, was never published.

There have been two further Observer's Books released since 1982. Book 99, Observer's Books, and book 100, Wayside and Woodland. Neither of these titles form part of the original series as they were not published by Frederick Warne & Co., so they are generally considered to be much less desirable and for completists only.

▲ Zoo Animals (no. 45). 1978 reprint. (g). Sold August 2009: £10

▲ Wild Flowers (no. 2). 1961 reprint. (g). Sold August 2009: £4.70

▲ Trees (no. 4). 1966 reprint. (g). Sold June 2009: £8.10

▲ Geology (no. 10). 1968 reprint. (g). Sold June 2009: £4.10

▲ Birds (no. 1). 1971 reprint. (vg). Sold June 2009: £4.20

▲ Automobiles (no. 21). 1970. (g). Sold June 2009: £6.10

▲ Pond Life (no. 24). 1956 first edition. (g). Sold June 2009: £15

▲ Sculpture (no. 37). 1966. (vg-ex). Sold February 2009: £22.20

▲ Fly Fishing (no. 68). 1980 reprint. (vg). Sold February 2009: £25.10

▲ Astronomy (no. 32). 1974 repring. (vg). Sold June 2008: £8

PELHAM PUPPETS

Bob Pelham launched his famous Pelham Puppets in 1947 after serving in World War II. Approximately seven million Pelham Puppets were produced (during the 1970s, five thousand were made per week). Bob Pelham died in 1980 and his widow carried on the business until 1986. After that, Pelham Puppets changed hands four times before going into receivership in 1992.

It is quite often the case that the boxes for dolls and other toys were discarded by children, who saw no further use for them. However, this does not apply to Pelham Puppets. Because the puppets had strings that could easily become tangled, it was common for children to keep returning the puppets to their rightful boxes after playtime to keep them tidy. This is good news for all the collectors out there, who benefit from an increased chance of finding Pelham Puppets that are still in the original packaging, although it does mean a boxed Pelham is not as significant a find as (for example) a boxed Dinky diecast vehicle. Of course, the relative ease with which boxed examples can be found also means that any unboxed examples will be devalued.

The boxes are actually quite useful for helping to date the puppet inside. For example, the solid yellow box featuring the snake charmer on the side was used from 1962 until 1969. A bit of research goes a long way, and you could soon become quite an expert.

▲ Skeleton (SL). Boxed. (1955). (vg). Sold January 2009: £100.10

▲ Pinocchio (SL). Boxed. (1970). (g). Sold August 2009: £60.10

▲ Mitzi (SS). Boxed. (1970). (vg). Sold September 2007: £40.10

▲ Gretel (SL2). Boxed. (1980). (vg-ex). Sold May 2010: £35.10

PENGUIN BOOKS

If you are intending to collect Penguin books as an investment, then be warned; most books were produced in huge quantities, and are unlikely to be worth much. Only early examples, and first editions in good condition (with dust jackets where applicable), are likely to have a strong market value. Of course, if you are just collecting for fun, then Penguin books can be a lovely area to specialise in. Good reading copies can usually be picked up for relatively little expense and will provide hours of enjoyment.

▲ Lady Chatterley's Lover. 1960. (g). Sold March 2010: £5.10

▲ Trial and Error. 1947. (f). Sold March 2010: £1.10

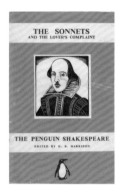

▲ The Sonnets. 1938. (g). Sold March 2009: £2.20

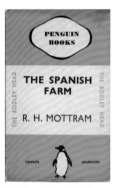

▲ The Spanish Farm. 1936. (g). Sold March 2010: £2.10

PETROLIANA

▲ Castrol enamel sign. (1950). 370 x 294mm. (g). Sold February 2011: £95.10

▲ Airfix Esso tank wagon. (1975). (ex). Sold June 2010: £6.60

▲ Esso pencil. (1960). (vg). Sold March 2010: £4

▲ Esso self-stick emblems. (1965). (vg). Sold June 2008: £6.10

▲ Pink Paraffin steel sign. 1961. 420 x 420mm. (g). Sold May 2008: £20.10

◀ BP button badge. (1960). (f-g). Sold June 2009: £4.40

◀ Shell button badge. (1960). (g-vg). Sold June 2009: £6

PHONECARDS

The rapid growth and popularity of mobile phones in the late-90s effectively put an end to the prolific use of phonecards.

In the phonecard heyday, producers such as British Telecom released numerous commemorative and definitive issues. Many of these are colourful and interesting, making them ideal collectables. Some issues are particularly rare and sought after by serious collectors. One of the most valuable cards is a 100 unit commemorative card from the 1977 Muirfield Open Golf Championship, which can sell for sums in excess of £3,000.

Many cards can complement other collectable subjects, for example: TV shows, James Bond, football, horseracing, etc.

BT produced some excellent Collectors' Packs. These generally contained a selection of cards with a face value of around £10. These packs were designed to be collectable items as well as serving the purpose of pre-paying telephone units.

Although phonecard collecting is commonly known as fusilately, in the United States it is referred to as telegery.

▲ Muppets Collectors Pack (BT). 1997. (mnt). Sold September 2010: £30.10

▲ The World is Not Enough (Eircom). 1999. (mnt). Sold September 2010: £5.10

▲ Disney's Pocahontas (Telecom Eireann). 1995. (vg). Sold September 2010: £3.10

▲ Radio Times (BT). 1994. (g). Sold February 2011: £3.10

▲ Pepsi. 1998. (vg). Sold February 2011: £3

▲ Woolworths (Mother's Day). (1995). (vg-ex). Sold March 2011: £5.10

▲ Today. (1995). (ex). Sold March 2011: £3

PIGGIN'

In 1993, wildlife artist David Corbridge was inspired to create a series of collectable ceramic pigs. He named the series Piggin'. The first one, Piggin' Tired, was released in 1993 by Collectible World Studios, who continued producing the loveable characters until 2006, when Xystos took over the range. There are now more than 250 different models.

Piggin' statues fall into the category of items that are specifically manufactured and marketed with collectors in mind. These items are definitely collectable, you can display them on your mantelpiece, and they look very nice; but they are unlikely to be the best investment.

So many of these statues are produced, and so many people purchase them and keep them in immaculate condition (either because they like them or because they think they could be worth something

▲ Piggin' Pouring Down. 1993. (vg). Sold July 2008: £10

one day), that they are never likely to become particularly scarce or valuable. They are definitely something to collect for fun rather than profit, although that does not mean to say that there won't be certain rare or limited edition pieces that will fetch decent sums on the secondary market.

THE PINK PANTHER

There's a multitude of Pink Panther collectables. Hardly surprising, given the popularity and cult status of the amiable cartoon character, coupled with the Peter Sellers connection.

Internet auctions are by far the best source but often the items will be at top asking price. Car boots provide the best source for bargain buys.

▲ In the Pink - James Galway & Henry Mancini (vinyl LP). 1984. (vg). Sold April 2011: £18.10

▲ Ceramic statue. (1980). (g-vg). Sold May 2008: £20

Among the list of collectable items that sell well are ceramics, diecast models, and film posters. Although of lesser interest, an extended list includes annuals, records, clocks, toys, DVDs, and videos.

A particularly interesting, albeit rather obscure item, is a Unigate milk bottle advertising Andrews Salts. The strap line is to take Andrews when you feel "off-colour," and the Pink Panther is cleverly portrayed in green.

The Pink Panther is such a well-known and popular character today that many people do not realise he was originally created by Hawley Pratt and Isadore "Friz" Freleng just to appear in the title sequence of a movie (Blake Edwards' 1963 classic crime caper The Pink Panther, which starred Peter Sellers as Inspector Clouseau).

The cartoon cat received better reviews than the film he introduced, and a series of animated shorts were put into production, the first of which, The Pink Phink, won an Academy Award.

Pink Panther continued to appear in introductions to all of the Inspector Clouseau sequels as well as being in his own movies and shows.

PLAYING CARDS

It sounds obvious, but if you are intending to purchase a deck of playing cards that has been opened, always make sure you check that all of the cards are present. Sometimes counting the cards is not enough, as unscrupulous traders will replace missing cards with cards from another set. Always check that the backs of all the cards in an open deck have the same design. Also, be cautious about the number of jokers in the pack. More and more people are getting involved in collecting joker cards, and this means more and more incomplete decks are appearing on the market. If you are selling lots of open decks, be sure to check that interested browsers are not removing joker cards when you aren't looking, as this will devalue your items.

Obviously, sealed decks of playing cards are the most desirable and will command the highest prices on the secondary market. If you do buy opened packs make sure the price is reasonable, and try not to buy well used or scruffy decks unless they are particularly cheap or rare. If there is no packaging at all for the cards, then invest in some acid-free plastic protectors to keep the cards in the best condition possible.

▲ Little Grey Rabbit. (1935). (g). Sold July 2008: £17.30

▲ Alwetha Raincoats. (1950). (f). Sold November 2008: £2.10

▲ Grant's Whisky. (2000). (ex). Sold July 2010: £5.60

▲ The Famous Hammer. 1996. (ex). Sold November 2009: £16.60

POLICE

There's a buoyant market for UK police collectables. Vintage items over 75 years old can fetch substantial sums. Collectors without deep pockets can still find reasonably priced, yet still very interesting, collectables from the 50s and 60s. Scour the better Collectors' Fairs for items, although perhaps the best source is the internet. Specialist clubs offer sales and swaps.

A word of warning: It is an offence to use Police items to impersonate a serving police officer. The Police Act (1996) covers the essential points. Basically, collectable items must be lawfully obtained and used for lawful purposes (therefore, collecting memorabilia for display is fine).

Various police forces have their own museums, containing artefacts, documents, and even old police vehicles.

▲ George V Long Service medal. 1918. (vg). Sold January 2011: £35.10

▲ Metropolitan Police enamel pin badge. (1960). (g). Sold January 2011: £12.70

▲ Modern Metropolitan Police helmet. (2000). (vg). Sold January 2011: £40

POP MUSIC

▲ Blue Oyster Cult concert ticket. 1989. (f-g). Sold February 2011: £1.60

▲ Dexy's Midnight Runners concert ticket. 1985. (g-vg). Sold February 2011: £3.60

▲ Camel concert ticket. 1975. (g-vg). Sold February 2011: £3.20

▲ No One Can Make My Sunshine Smile (Everly Brothers) sheet music. 1962. (vg). Sold January 2011: £6

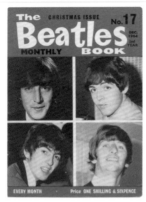

▲ The Beatles Book number 17. December 1964. (vg). Sold February 2011: £9.90

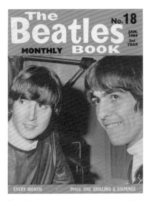

▲ The Beatles Book number 18. January 1965. (vg). Sold February 2011: £9.90

▲ Record Mirror no. 254. January 1966. (vg). Sold March 2010: £10.60

▲ Top Pop Stars (book). 1962. (g). Sold February 2011: £7.30

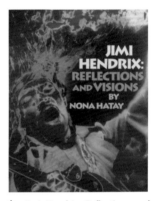

▲ Jimi Hendrix: Reflections and Visions (book). 1995. (vg). Sold February 2011: £5

▲ Elvis Costello pin badge. (1975). (vg). Sold September 2007: £1.30

▲ Stray Cats badge. (1980). (vg). Sold March 2008: £1.20

POST OFFICE

(Front)   (Reverse)

▲ Post Office savings tin. 1981. (g-vg). Sold November 2009: £10.40

▲ Post Office telegram. 1953. (g). Sold June 2010: £3

▲ Post Office phonecard. (1995). (ex). Sold March 2011: £1

▲ Post office enamel brass badge. (1965). (vg). Sold August 2005: £6

POSTAL ORDERS

Postal orders were introduced on 1 January 1881. Until April 2006 they were issued in fixed denominations, but after this date they could be issued in any amount, similar to a personal cheque.

This is a rather niche (but growing) market area.

▲ 2/6d. 1942. (f-g). Sold May 2009: £12.20

▲ 10/-. 1966. (vg). Sold May 2009: £12.20

▲ 5/-. 1965. (vg). Sold May 2009: £20.90

POSTCARDS

The earliest known postcards were private cards patented in 1861 by John P. Charlton of Philadelphia, who later transferred the copyright to H. Lipman. Although these were the first "postal cards," official cards issued by the Post Office were not introduced until 1869, in Austria.

The Post Office introduced postcards to Britain in 1870. They were simple, plain cards with a pre-printed stamp. The address had to be written on one side, and the message had to be written on the reverse; a system which stayed in place for over thirty years.

In 1894, the Post Office made an announcement that as of 1 September, private cards could be published and sent through the post as long as a halfpenny stamp was affixed. This new freedom encouraged companies to produce their own cards, and many began to include pictures to stand out from the crowd. There is evidence to suggest the first publisher to produce picture cards was George Stewart and Co. of Edinburgh.

In 1895, cards of size 4.75 inches x 3.5 inches (known as "court cards") became standard, and this remained the case until 1899, when the size of 5.5 inches x 3.5 inches became the norm. Quite often the image on the front of the card would take up almost all of the available space, leaving hardly any room at all for a small note or message to be written. This reduced the usefulness of the card as a means of communication; and because the picture had to be small to allow for a message the cards were not handsome enough for people to appreciate them as collectable art.

It was not until 1902 that the Post Office changed its regulations to allow a message and address to appear on the same side of the card. This was a revolutionary change, leading to the creation of "divided backs," where the backs of postcards were divided with a straight line running vertically down the centre. Now the message could be written on the left, and the address could be written on the right, leaving the other side of the card free for lavish artwork or photographs.

It was this revolutionary change that created a boom in the popularity of picture postcards, as it was now possible for elaborate designs to be employed that covered the whole of one side of the card.

▲   Snow White. 1938. (vg). Sold September 2009: £90

▲ Leather greetings card. (1900). (g-vg). Sold September 2009: £15

▲   "Something stinks..." (1940). (vg). Sold September 2009: £7.10

▲ Boulter's Lock. (1910). (g). Sold May 2009: £8.60

▲ Great Fire at the Anchor Maltings. 1907. (g-vg). Sold May 2009: £12.90

The change ushered in the "Golden Age," when postcards were a common form of communication and many people had collections.

Great Britain was the first country to issue "divided back" postcards in 1902. France introduced "divided back" cards in 1904, Germany in 1905, and America in 1907. After these dates, some manufacturers did continue to print cards with margins on the front for messages to be written, but these were quickly phased out.

From a contemporary collector's point of view, the change to "divided back" is something of a blessing for a number of reasons. One of the most obvious reasons is that people stopped writing over the front of postcards, so any "divided back" cards tend to be much more attractive. However, the most important reason is that it was only once these cards were introduced that people really began to start collecting seriously and preserving cards so that we are still able to enjoy them today.

The First World War brought a sudden end to the "Golden Age." The fine printed cards from Germany and other European countries were no longer available, and home production was significantly reduced. Increased use of telephones also played a part, and the hobby never recovered.

Since that time postcards have become more associated with holidays and seaside resorts. Happy holidaymakers send the little works of art to all the friends and loved ones who couldn't be with them, but postcards are rarely used for any other reason. However, the hobby of collecting is becoming more and more popular, and early postcards are significantly increasing in value, thanks not only to their attractive appearance but also to their historical significance. Perhaps this is the beginning of a second "Golden Age."

Cards that attract the most interest (and therefore usually sell for the highest sums) include novelty cards (featuring flaps, moving parts, ribbons and other embellishments), military cards, silks, leather cards, cards featuring well-known characters (such as Snow White), and cards illustrated by popular artists. Obviously, condition is very important, but a certain amount of creases, scuffs, and marks is acceptable on old, rare examples.

▲ World War I novelty. (1915). (vg). Sold May 2009: £20

▲ Slubbing. (1905). (vg). Sold July 2009: £6

▲ Oxfordshire and Buckinghamshire Light Infantry. 1909. (g). Sold November 2009: £10.60

▲ Louis Wain illustration. 1922. (g-vg). Sold November 2009: £18

▲ "A nice plaice." 1937. (f-g). Sold November 2009: £1.10

▲ Bull Ring, Birmingham. (1938). (vg). Sold March 2011: £11

▲ Flight of Henri Farman. 1909. (g). Sold March 2011: £13

▲ Middlesbrough transporter bridge. (1925). (vg). Sold March 2011: £6.30

▲ The Morris Minor. 1954. (vg). Sold February 2011: £15.20

▲ Ye Olde Cheshire Cheese (Fleet Street). (1910). (vg). Sold January 2011: £7.40

▲ Popular Songs Illustrated. 1903. (f-g). Sold January 2011: £4.10

▲ Fry's Chocolate (Five Boys). (1910). (g). Sold November 2010: £26.70

▲ Scot's Emulsion. (1910). (vg). Sold November 2010: £7.90

▲ Berry Head House. (1920). (g). Sold September 2010: £13

▲ Col Royston questioning Indunas. 1906. (g-vg). Sold June 2010: £20.70

POSTMARKS

Sometimes the stamps and cancellations on a postcard can be more interesting than the actual card. There are plenty of people who specialise in collecting postmarks and fine used stamps, and postcards can be a fantastic resource for such collectors.

An interesting postcard with an equally interesting stamp and cancellation is likely to generate a lot of interest when it goes up for sale. If cancellations are thematically linked to the card in some way this can also add interest and value (for example, there is a certain amount of humour evident in a postcard depicting dogs that has an affixed stamp cancelled with an Isle of Dogs postmark). Postcards with stamps affixed that were cancelled on the first day of issue fall into the category of First Day Covers, and these will also be of particular interest.

It certainly pays to check the stamps and postmarks on any postcards you find at a boot sale or collectors' fair, as what at first appears to be rather dull and uninteresting could actually tell a fabulous story, and be of historical significance.

▲ Road accidents slogan on lettercard. 1962. (g). Sold December 2008: £1.10

▲ Swiss airmail postmarks on envelope. 1943. (f). Sold April 2008: £3

POT LIDS

▲ Burgess's Anchovy Paste. (1880). (g). Sold September 2008: £12.20

▲ Holloway's Ointment. (1890). (g). Sold September 2008: £12

In the mid-nineteenth century, retailers of paste-like products for domestic consumption marketed them in glazed stoneware pots. Such pots were originally covered with greaseproof paper or a plain glazed stoneware lid.

Enterprising manufacturers hit on the idea of using the stoneware lids to advertise the products. By the turn of the century they had reached the height of their popularity. It is these pot lids that collectors are interested in and the beauty of collecting these lids is that they can be purchased relatively cheaply and can even be dug up in old rubbish dumps at no cost at all.

The majority of examples are black on white but full-colour examples are plentiful. The easiest and cleanest method of acquiring them is from car boot sales, collectors' fairs, and the internet. Like all collectables, value is affected by condition and rarity, and some really hard to find examples can be worth as much as £100. The most common product is toothpaste.

There are books on the subject of collecting pot lids and these can be found in libraries or on the internet.

PREMIUM BONDS

▲ £5 premium bond. 1977. (g-vg).
Sold September 2007: £3

▲ £1 premium bond. 1958. (g). Sold
September 2007: £1

▲ £2 premium bond. 1973. (g-vg).
Sold August 2007: £1.50

▲ £1 premium bond. (1963). (g). Sold
January 2006: £4

RADIOS

▲ Fortune AM shirt pocket radio (1970). (vg).
Sold June 2008: £11

Miniature transistors (known as Shirt pocket radios) are popular among radio enthusiasts because of their compact size. They were mainly made in Japan, China, Hong Kong and the USA (British names such as "Pye" were foreign manufactured).

You can find pocket radios at specialist fairs, including the large ones organised by the British Vintage Wireless Society. You can also find them through specialist magazines and internet auctions.

▲ Osram radio valve. (1930).
(vg). Sold September 2009: £2.20

▲ Mazda radio valve. (1970). (vg).
Sold September 2009: £2.10

▲ Wonder shirt pocket radio. (1975). (vg). Sold
June 2008: £11

RAILWAYANA

Anything relating to railways can generally be expected to attract some interest in an auction. Of particular interest are old metal signs, from station platforms and engines, but these can prove to be rather expensive.

However, collecting items relating to railways need not always be an overly-expensive practice. There are plenty of books, tickets, maps, and guides that can all be picked up for reasonable sums.

Old books and pieces of ephemera are much easier to store and post than heavy metal signs and pieces from genuine steam locomotives, and they can also represent a sound investment.

There are hundreds of books for railway enthusiasts. Some are extremely specialised and, as long as the right person spots your books for sale, you can sell for many times the cost price. The best place to buy is a car boot sale. Some traders sell books by the van-load. In particular, look out for books published by Ian Allan. Ian Allan Publishing was established in 1942 and specialises in books and magazines related to transport. Such books are in demand, and good, clean examples can often be expected to sell well. The first book the company ever produced was ABC of Southern Locomotives, and a first edition will be of much interest to any railwayana enthusiast.

Some people interested in railwayana will want to start a collection of mechanical model trains; this can be a good choice, as model trains are incredibly popular and often sell well. Collecting model railways is such a large subject that it is a collecting category in its own right (see page 83).

If you simply don't have the space for a mechanical train track, then you might want to consider static model trains instead. Such models will look fantastic on display, and they are not the largest or heaviest items to post should you try to sell them in the future.

▲ Marshall's Book of Railways (hardback book). 1961. (vg). Sold January 2011: £4.60

▲ A Regional History of the Railways of Great Britain, Vol 2 (hardback book). 1961. (vg). Sold January 2011: £4.20

▲ British Pacific Locomotives (hardback book). 1962. (vg). Sold January 2011: £5

▲ The Ian Allan Book of Railways (hardback book). 1962. (g-vg). Sold November 2010: £4.10

▲ A Breath of Steam: Vol 1 (hardback book). 1975. (g-vg). Sold November 2010: £4

▲ Railway Roundabout (Ian Allan hardback book). (1960). (vg). Sold November 2010: £8.40

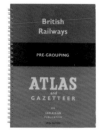

▲ British Railways Pre-Grouping Atlas and Gazetteer (Ian Allan hardback book). 1973. (vg). Sold November 2010: £6

▲ Midland Album (hardback book). (vg-ex). Sold May 2011: £3

▲ George V Locomotive metal number and registration plates. 1962. (vg). Did not sell at £180 start price in August 2010.

▲ Cast iron wagon plate. 1956. (f). Sold November 2010: £25.10

▲ Cast iron GWR bridge plate. (g). Sold November 2010: £145.10

▲ Cast iron station master sign. (1925). (g-vg). Sold November 2010: £180.10

▲ Piccadilly Line Extension postcard. (1980). (vg). Sold March 2010: £6.10

▲ Camden Town Engine House postcard. 1914. (f). Sold March 2010: £4.10

▲ Schools Class 220SR static model. 2002. (ex). Sold April 2011: £6.60

▲ Battle of Britain Class static model. 2006. (vg). Sold November 2010: £20.10

▲ Duchess LMS static model. 2004. (vg). Sold November 2010: £20.10

▲ Britannia Class static model. 2006. (vg). Sold November 2010: £20.10

▲ LNER "Flying Scotsman" static model. 2001. (ex). Sold November 2010: £15.10

▲ A4 Class "Mallard" static model. 2001. (ex). Sold November 2010: £15.10

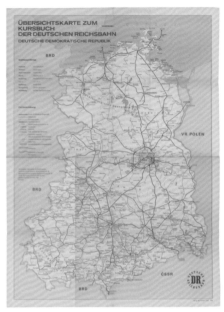

▲ East German Railway map. 1985. (vg). Sold April 2011: £3

▲ North Eastern Railway 3rd class travel pass. 1917. (f). Sold March 2011: £15

▲ British Railways steamer reservation notice. 1952. (g). Sold March 2011: £2

▲ Railway Magazine. December 1963. (g-vg). Sold April 2011: £3.10

▲ Trains Illustrated (magazine). August 1957. (vg). Sold March 2010: £10.10

▲ Railway World (magazine). March 1964. (g-vg). Sold April 2011: £3.10

▲ British Railways wages card. 1954. (vg). Sold April 2011: £2

▲ British Railways 2nd Class weekly season ticket. 1970. (g). Sold April 2011: £2.10

▲ LNER goods train label. 1944. (vg). Sold April 2011: £4.30

RECORDS (45s)

▲ Walk Don't Run – The Ventures. 1960. Vinyl (vg), sleeve (f). Sold March 2011: £5.20

▲ No Time – The Northern Lights. 1966. Vinyl (g), sleeve (f). Sold March 2011: £12.50

▲ Can't Help Falling in Love – Elvis Presley. 1961. Vinyl (vg), sleeve (g). Sold March 2011: £5.20

▲ See My Friend – The Kinks. 1965. Vinyl (vg), sleeve (g-vg). Sold March 2011: £4.70

▲ Ob-La-Di, Ob-La-Da – The Bedrocks. 1968. Vinyl (vg), sleeve (vg). Sold March 2011: £5.80

▲ Something Here in My Heart – The Paper Dolls. 1968. Vinyl (g), sleeve (g). Sold March 2011: £4.80

▲ A Whiter Shade of Pale – Procol Harum. 1967. Vinyl (vg), sleeve (vg). Sold February 2011: £4.10

▲ Heart of a Teenage Girl – Craig Douglas. 1960. Vinyl (g-vg), repro sleeve (ex). Sold February 2011: £6.60

▲ Cinderella Rockefella – Esther & Abi Ofarim. 1967. Vinyl (g), sleeve (g-vg). Sold February 2011: £5.20

▲ Who Are You – The Who. 1978. Dinked. Vinyl (g-vg), sleeve (vg). Sold February 2011: £7.70

▲ Barbara Ann – The Regents. 1961. Vinyl (vg), sleeve (g). Sold February 2011: £10.10

▲ Just a Little Bit – The Undertakers. 1964. Vinyl (g-vg), repro sleeve (ex). Sold November 2010: £16.90

▲ Eve of Destruction – Barry McGuire. 1965. Vinyl (g), sleeve (g-vg). Sold September 2010: £10.20

▲ Yesterday Has Gone – Cupids Inspriation. 1968. Dinked. Vinyl (g), sleeve (f). Sold August 2010: £4.30

▲ The Jean Genie – David Bowie. 1972. Vinyl (g-vg), sleeve (vg). Sold August 2010: £4.20

▲ It's Over – Roy Orbison. 1964. Vinyl (vg), sleeve (g). Sold July 2010: £10.10

▲ Got to Get You Into My Life – Cliff Bennett. 1966. Vinyl (vg), sleeve (g). Sold March 2010: £6.10

▲ That's What Love Will Do – Joe Brown. 1963. Vinyl (g-vg), sleeve (g). Sold March 2010: £5.10

▲ Then He Kissed Me – The Crystals. 1963. Vinyl (p-f), sleeve (f). Sold March 2010: £5.50

▲ Star in My Life – Steve Marriott. 1976. Vinyl (vg), sleeve (vg). Sold March 2010: £3.10

RECORDS (EPs)

▲ Thunderbirds Are Go! – Cliff Richard and the Shadows. 1966. Vinyl (g-vg), sleeve (f). Sold April 2011: £40

▲ Queen's First EP. 1976. Vinyl (vg), sleeve (vg). Sold April 2011: £6.60

▲ History of a Boy Scout – The Dave Brubeck Quartet. 1963. Vinyl (vg), sleeve (g). Sold April 2011: £6.70

▲ Dickie Valentine Swings. 1963. Vinyl (vg), sleeve (f). Sold March 2011: £5.60

▲ Lawrence of Arabia. 1963. Vinyl (ex), sleeve (vg). Sold March 2011: £7.10

▲ It's So Easy – The Crickets. 1959. Vinyl (g-vg), sleeve (g). Sold February 2011: £40.10

▲ The Sound of Cyril Davies. 1963. Vinyl (g-vg), sleeve (ex). Sold February 2011: £50

▲ The Fabulous Platters. 1956. Vinyl (vg), sleeve (vg). Sold January 2011: £7.30

▲ Adam Faith. 1961. Vinyl (vg), sleeve (g). Sold November 2010: £15.30

▲ The Late Great Buddy Holly. 1961. Vinyl (vg), sleeve (vg). Sold November 2010: £30.10

▲ Bobby Vee's Biggest Hits. 1963. Vinyl (g-vg), sleeve (vg). Sold November 2010: £13.60

▲ Rock Around the Clock – Bill Haley and His Comets. 1956. Vinyl (g-vg), sleeve (g). Sold November 2010: £14.30

▲ The Cheers. 1956. Dinked. Vinyl (vg), sleeve (f-g). Sold September 2010: £40

▲ The Spotnicks in Paris. 1963. Vinyl (vg), sleeve (g). Sold August 2010: £20.90

▲ Mrs Brown You've Got a Lovely Daughter – Herman's Hermits. 1964. Vinyl (vg), sleeve (vg). Sold August 2010: £15

▲ Roy Orbison's Stage Show Hits. 1961. Vinyl (vg), sleeve (vg). Sold July 2010: £35.10

▲ Expresso Bongo – Cliff Richard. 1960. Vinyl (vg), sleeve (g). Sold July 2010: £12

▲ PJ's Hits – PJ Proby. 1964. Vinyl (vg), sleeve (g-vg). Sold July 2010: £15.10

▲ Helen – Helen Shapiro. 1961. Vinyl (vg), sleeve (g). Sold June 2010: £15.10

▲ Got LIVE if you Want It! – The Rolling Stones. 1965. Vinyl (vg), sleeve (g). Sold June 2010: £15

RECORDS (LPs)

▲ Live! At the Star Club – The Beatles. 1962. Vinyl (vg-ex), sleeve (vg-ex). Sold April 2010: £15.10

▲ Dark Horse – George Harrison. 1974. Vinyl (vg-ex), sleeve (vg). Sold April 2010: £4

▲ Django Reinhardt & Stephane Grappelly. (1960). Vinyl (vg), sleeve (vg). Sold September 2010: £5.30

▲ The Best of Cilla Black. 1968. Vinyl (vg), sleeve (vg). Sold February 2011: £2.30

▲ Electric Ladyland – The Jimi Hendrix Experience. 1968. Vinyl (g), sleeve (g). Sold February 2011: £8.70

▲ Apples, Peaches, Pumpkin Pie – Jay & The Techniques.1967. Vinyl (g), sleeve (vg). Sold November 2010: £15.10

▲ Roustabout – Elvis. 1964. Vinyl (g), sleeve (g). Sold November 2010: £5

▲ Sounds of Silence – Simon & Garfunkel. 1965. Vinyl (vg), sleeve (vg). Sold November 2010: £2

▲ Don't Knock the Twist – Chubby Checker. 1961. Vinyl (vg), sleeve (vg). Sold November 2010: £5

▲ Rubber Soul – The Beatles. 1965. Vinyl (g-vg), sleeve (g-vg). Sold November 2010: £15.20

▲ Greatest Hits – ABBA. 1976. Vinyl (vg), sleeve (vg). Sold November 2010: £2.10

▲ The Sound of Music – Original London Cast. 1961. Vinyl (vg), sleeve (vg). Sold November 2010: £12.10

ROYALTY

There are certain royal "celebrities" who garner a lot more interest than others. Generally speaking, the more popular the family member is, the more merchandise will be available. This is a double-edged sword, as the merchandise will not usually appreciate much in value, but at least there is a lot to choose from. It is arguable that collecting under the theme of Royalty, more so than any other collecting subject, demands that you perform a fine balancing act between collecting for profit and collecting for fun.

Diana memorabilia is, of course, exceptionally popular and rather easy to find. This is great news for collectors, who should have no trouble quickly building a good array of items, but it is not such great news for those who are looking to buy items with a strong investment potential.

▲ Royal visit to Blackpool (postcard). 1913. (g-vg). Sold June 2010: £18.80

▲ Changing Guard at Buckingham Palace (postcard). 1953. (vg). Sold June 2010: £4.60

▲ Princess Elizabeth and Philip Mountbatten wedding programme. 1947. (g-vg). Sold March 2010: £11.70

▲ Telegram from Buckingham Palace. 1960. (g-vg). Sold March 2010: £6

▲ Pakistan Royal Visit commemorative cover. 1961. (vg). Sold March 2010: £8.10

(Obverse)

(Reverse)

▲ Queen Victoria Florin. 1887. (g-vg). Sold March 2010: £20.10

▲ Royal Tour of Canada (limpback book). 1951. (g). Sold November 2010: £2

▲ Queen Victoria autograph. No dedication. Sold April 2011: £100.10

▲ Princess Diana phonecards. (1997). (vg). Sold February 2011: £3.10 each

▲ Coronation souvenir tin. 1911. (f-g). Sold June 2010: £15

▲ King George the Sixth (limpback book). 1951. (vg). Sold June 2010: £5.10

▲ Queen Elizabeth (limpback book). (1952). (vg). Sold June 2010: £2

▲ Coronation of Her Majesty Queen Elizabeth II souvenir programme. 1953. (vg). Sold June 2010: £8

RUGBY

▲ England v Scotland programme. 1977. (vg). Sold October 2007: £6

▲ England v South Africa programme. 1952. (g-vg). Sold March 2010: £15.10

▲ World Cup souvenir guide. 2000. (g). Sold September 2008: £2.30

▲ Welsh Rugby Union ashtray. 1980. (vg). Sold March 2010: £5.10

▲ Rugby League Centenary First Day Cover. 1995. (ex). Sold October 2007: £6

▲ Rugby Super12 souvenir miniature rugby ball. (1996). (vg). Sold June 2006: £1.10

▲ Table Rugby Subbuteo (incomplete). 1970. (g). Sold December 2006: £2.50

RUPERT THE BEAR

Rupert Bear first appeared in the Daily Express on 8 November 1920. He was first drawn by Mary Tourtel, but Alfred Bestall took over in 1935. During the height of his popularity in the 1950s, sales of Rupert annuals topped 1.7 million, and today the Rupert annual is still one of the best-selling annuals sold worldwide.

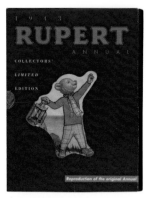

▲ Reproduction 1943 annual. 1995. (vg). Sold December 2008: £8.60

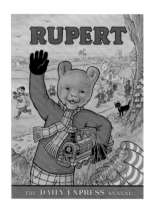

▲ Rupert annual. 1976. (vg). Sold September 2008: £15

▲ Rupert annual. 1978. (f). Sold July 2008: £6

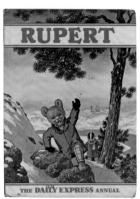

▲ Rupert annual. 1970. (g). Sold July 2008: £12.10

▲ Rupert annual. 1964. (g). Sold June 2008: £20.20

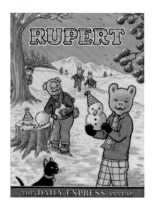

▲ Rupert annual. 1974. (vg) Sold May 2008: £10

▲ Rupert Scammell 6-Wheeler diecast model (Lledo). (1990). (vg). Sold August 2010: £7

▲ Rupert jigsaw. (1970). (f). Sold November 2009: £9

SCOUTS & GUIDES

▲ Diamond Jubilee of Scouting commemorative cover. 1967. (g). Sold February 2008: £5.10

▲ Gibraltar Scout Association First Day Cover. 1960. (g). Sold November 2008: £2.10

▲ The Scout Song Book. 1958. (f). September 2007: £4

▲ The Scout Annual. 1969. (g). Sold February 2008: £3

▲ Scout Handbook. 1967. (g). Sold February 2008: £2.10

▲ The Brownie Annual. 1976. (vg). Sold November 2008: £4.30

▲ Cub Scouts Ladybird book. 1973. (f) Sold November 2008: £1.50

▲ The Guide Handbook. 1989. (f). Sold November 2008: £1.20

▲ Hackney Scout Song Book. 1931. (p). Sold September 2009: £2.20

▲ The Scout (magazine). 1955. (vg). Sold February 2011: £1

▲ Chief Scout's Visit cloth pennant. 1962. (g-vg). Sold February 2008: £9

▲ Girl Guides photograph. (1920). (vg). Sold November 2008: £1

SHAVING

Some of the most collectable items in the category of shaving are old razor blades. Collecting razor blades is enhanced by the colourful packets produced by the multitude of companies who traded in them. This is a perfect collecting area if you are on a budget, and as an added bonus, your collection will be extremely easy to store. Good sources are the big collectors' fairs.

If you intend to collect razorblades, then obviously it is very important that you keep your collection safely out of harm's way (especially if children could get hold of them). Putting your blades in a glass picture frame not only keeps them safe, but also creates a very pleasant display piece that is sure to be a talking point for visitors.

RAZOR BLADES

▲ Packard. (1935). (ex). Sold February 2009: £3.50

▲ Personna. (1935). (ex). Sold Febuary 2009: £3.50

7 O'Clock. (1955). (g). Sold February 2009: £5.10

▲ Razorbill. (1935). (vg). Sold February 2009: £5.10

▲ Swan. (1925). (g). Sold February 2009: £3.50

▲ Nacet. (1950). (ex). Sold February 2009: £3.50

▲ Bluebird. (1935). (vg). Sold February 2009: £3.50

▲ Philishave SC7970 cordless razor. 1963. (g-vg). Sold September 2009: £5

▲ Viceroy Dry Shaver. 1936. (g). Sold February 2006: £3

▲ Rolls Razor Strop Dressing. (1940). (g-vg). Sold November 2008: £4.60

▲ Quadruple strop. (1940). (f). Sold November 2008: £5.90

▲ Remington electric shaver. (1965). (g). Sold March 2007: £1

SHIPPING (NAUTICALIA)

▲ HMS Beaver (postcard). (1913). (f). Sold April 2011: £6.10

▲ Belgian Navy cloth badge. (1970). (g-vg). Sold January 2011: £2.10

▲ Argentine Navy cloth badge. (1970). (g). Sold January 2011: £1.80

▲ Twickenham Ferry (postcard). 1944. (vg). Sold April 2011: £4.10

▲ Fleet Air Arm (book). 1942. (vg). Sold February 2011: £12.10

▲ His Majesty's Minesweepers. 1943. (g). Sold November 2010: £7.60

▲ Empress of Canada (postcard). 1952. (g).Sold April 2011: £4.10

▲ Morning prayers on St Vincent training ship (postcard). 1904. (f). Sold January 2011: £7.10

▲ Submarines at Calais (postcard). (1918). (g-vg). Sold January 2011: £5.10

▲ Empress of Canada menu card. 1970. (vg). Sold April 2011: £3.10

SMOKERAMA

The subject of smokerama covers those items that are related to the act of smoking but which do not specifically relate to any particular tobacco company. For example, postcards depicting people smoking would be classed as smokerama, while postcards depicting an advertisement for Capstan cigarettes would be classed as tobacciana.

▲ "Caught smoking" (postcard). 1908. (g). Sold April 2010: £6.10

▲ Child smoking (postcard). (1910). (vg-ex). Sold May 2011: £10.10

▲ Pipe knife. (1975). (vg). Sold February 2008: £4.80

▲ Pipe case. (1950). (f). Sold January 2007: £0.40

▲ Cigarette ration card. 1946. (g). Sold October 2006: £9.70

▲ Cigarette case. (1960). (g). Sold December 2005: £4.90

SNOOPY

▲ Snoopy soap (boxed). (1980). (vg). Sold May 2008: £3.20

▲ Wind-up Snoopy (boxed). (1975). (g). Sold April 2008: £14.20

Snoopy is a character from the long-running comic strip Peanuts. The comic was created by Charles M Schulz, and ran from 2 October 1950 until 13 February 2000 (the day after Schulz passed away following complications from colon cancer). While Snoopy started out as a rather ordinary beagle under the guardianship of Charlie Brown, he quickly developed some odd character traits and arguably became the strip's biggest star. He became something of a daydreamer, and he could often be found in dark sunglasses, hanging out at the Student Union under the alias "Joe Cool," or battling the Red Baron in desperate aerial combat.

Those of us interested in collecting Peanuts (or specifically Snoopy) merchandise have a lot to keep us busy. As well as 17,897 comic strips, Charlie Brown and the gang appeared in television advertisements, books, several television shows, and more than 30 very memorable feature-length TV specials.

SNOWGLOBES

▲ Sydney souvenir. (1990). (vg). Sold June 2008: £3.20

▲ Big Ben souvenir. (1990). (vg). Sold June 2008: £5.20

SPEEDWAY

Programmes are the number one recommendation in this category, particularly the very early ones (1920s – 1940s) in good condition. Programmes dated 1990+ are generally not of much interest but are still worth acquiring for a few pence to put into storage. Enamel pin badges are also desirable and, again, the older the better.

It is best to concentrate on UK Speedway, and to look out for those clubs and circuits that no longer exist.

▲ Speedway model. (1980). (f). Sold July 2005: £8.10

▲ Speedway Annual. 1950. (f-g).Sold June 2005: £10.70

▲ Speedway Star Silver Jubilee badge. 1977. (g-vg). Sold June 2005: £2

▲ Belle Vue v Wembley programme. 1952. (g). Sold January 2006: £5.30

▲ Wolverhampton v Belle Vue programme. 1971. (g). Sold May 2008: £3

▲ West Ham v Cradley Heath programme. 1968. (g-vg). Sold May 2008: £3.90

▲ Swindon v Coventry programme. 1963. (g-vg). Sold May 2011: £3.30

▲ Leicester v Ipswich programme. 1975. (g). Sold February 2009: £2.30

▲ Newport programme. 1968. (vg). Sold August 2010: £4.10

▲ Best Pairs Trophy programme. 1967. (vg). Sold November 2011: £4.10

▲ Ipswich programme. 1960. (g). Sold August 2010: £4.40

SPOONS

▲ Bethlehem souvenir. (1970). (g). Sold Mach 2009: £4.90

▲ Jerusalem souvenir. (1970). (g). Sold March 2009: £3.10

▲ NSW Christmas souvenir. 1990. (vg). Sold March 2009: £4.80

▲ Silver Jubilee commemorative souvenir. 1977. (vg). Sold November 2008: £7.90

▲ Minnie Mouse. (1970). (vg). Sold June 2008: £5.20

STAR TREK

▲ Star Trek Annual. 1975. (vg). Sold May 2011: £4

▲ Star Trek Annual. 1978. (vg). Sold May 2011: £3

▲ Star Trek Annual. 1979. (vg). Sold May 2011: £3

▲ Star Trek VI – The Undiscovered Country (DVD). 2001. (mnt). Sold December 2006: £4.50

(cover)   (inside)

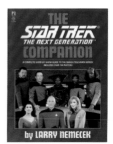

▲ The Borg phonecard presentation pack. 1996. (mnt). Sold March 2011: £15

▲ Star Trek key ring. 1998. (ex). Sold December 2008: £2.30

▲ The Star Trek: The Next Generation Companion (book). 1992. (g). Sold October 2006: £2.80

▲ Star Wars: Young Readers' Edition (book). 1978. (g). Sold October 2007: £1.50

▲ Anthony Daniels autographed picture of C-3PO. No dedication. Sold September 2007: £11.10

Young visionary George Lucas, bloody, beaten, but unbowed by intense levels of stress during production, finally released his "space opera" in the summer of 1977. Escalating production costs during the shoot had pushed the budget from an agreed $8million to $11million. Most of the crew didn't "get" the movie and hadn't taken it seriously. Mark Hamill was involved in a car accident, and the resulting facial injuries he received meant reshoots had not been possible. Harrison Ford thought the movie was weird, and claimed the dialogue was unspeakable. It looked like it was going to be a disaster. It wasn't.

Fast-forward more than 30 years, and you would be hard-pressed to name a more influential movie, or one that has spawned such an epic franchise. Six movies, one "Holiday Special," various spin-off movies about the Ewoks, and several cartoon series have generated a wealth of memorabilia, both old and new, and where to begin a collection is often daunting.

Name something – anything – and it is more than likely it has been made with Star Wars branding at some point. There are computer and video games, books, comics, graphic novels, pencil sharpeners, notebooks, chess sets, board games, bubble bath, pencils, watches, mugs, action figures, and more. It can be a baffling minefield, and there is plenty of fake memorabilia out there to trick the unwary collector.

The original series of action figures, produced by Kenner from 1977 until 1985, are generally considered to be the most interesting and most desirable Star Wars merchandise. Find a collector of Star Wars memorabilia and he or she is sure to have at least one Kenner figure somewhere.

Commonly referred to as the 3¾inch scale figures, this fantastic range of toys offered over 100 posable heroes and villains, plus lots of oddly out-of-scale vehicles and play sets, enabling a whole generation of children to recreate their favourite movie scenes.

Of course, as with many toys, it is becoming increasingly difficult to find good condition examples. The figures were often played with until they broke, and then they were discarded. Those that have survived are generally missing their accessories, have faded, or have limbs that have worked loose. For this reason, collecting the action figures can be quite a task, and you may need deep pockets to get a complete set.

One of the many problems facing a collector is finding figures that are still in the original

▲ Obi-Wan Kenobi Kenner figure. 1977. (vg). Sold September 2007: £8.10

▲ Darth Vader Kenner figure. 1977. (vg). Sold September 2007: £6

packaging. As with many toys at the time, Star Wars figures were sold in blister backs (the figure is sealed on a piece of backing card with vacuum-formed plastic). This type of packaging is notoriously difficult to open without causing damage. You can safely assume that if a figure was opened for play, then the packaging will not have survived the ordeal.

What this means from a collecting standpoint is, although sealed figures command a premium, there is still a very healthy market for figures that are no longer in their packaging, as long as the figures have been well looked after and still have all of their original accessories.

Note that this only applies to the figures. Play sets and vehicles were boxed, and it is possible to find 'played with' examples that still have boxes and all of the original instruction sheets.

▲ Star Wars Trilogy VHS box set. 1997. (mnt). Sold September 2009: £10.20

Although an excited child is likely to have ripped into a blister pack and completely destroyed it in the process, those who take a bit of care might be able to remove the figure in such a way that the pack can be resealed afterwards. This opens up two possible avenues for the artful scammer. Action figures can be removed, altered slightly to appear rarer than they are (given a different coloured cloak or "weapon"), and then carefully resealed to give the impression they have never been opened. Alternatively, the pack can be resealed in such a way that up close it has clearly been opened and damaged, but in a photograph it looks as new. Sellers can misrepresent items in this manner in online internet auctions, using descriptions such as "on backing card" rather than saying "mint condition, sealed in original packaging" An avid collector will tell you there is a big difference in terms of price between a pack that has been opened and then glued back together, and a pack that is in mint "off the shelf" condition, but by the time you have received your purchase, it could be too late to complain.

▲ Return of the Jedi sticker album (complete). 1983. (g). Sold October 2006: £9.60

Misrepresentation in online auctions is always a concern that a collector should be cautious of. In auctions, particularly those without pictures, clever descriptions can make items sound very different. Good examples of this are making one of the new Hasbro action figures sound like a vintage Kenner action figure, or making a Galoob Micro Machines vehicle (about the size of a 50p coin) sound like a large-scale vintage toy.

With each release of a Star Wars movie, there is a massive amount of publicity and advertising. Premiums (free promotional items) have always been a strong element of the Star Wars phenomenon, and there is a huge range of inexpensive and often quite fun items for the casual collector to acquire.

Magazines around the time of a movie's premiere can usually be found giving away free colour supplements; various confectionery companies will be offering toys and gimmicks to those willing to collect and send off a few coupons; most fast food chains will be offering something to those who have dropped in for a burger and fries. It's a massive collecting area

▲ Darth Vader bubble bath. 1977. (g). Sold January 2006: £9.30

in its own right, and in some cases the items can be rather good quality and attractive display pieces.

However, a note of caution: While most premiums are cheap to acquire, and readily available, you must always remember that Star Wars is an international phenomenon. Premiums released in the UK are different from those of other countries. It is a more than daunting task to attempt to acquire complete sets of every type of premium from every country, and you would be wise to limit your collecting to certain countries or themes.

▲ Star Wars LP. 1977. Vinyl (g-vg), sleeve (g-vg). Sold September 2005: £5

On 17 November 1978 the Star Wars Holiday Special was aired on television for the first, and last, time.

The show starred Chewbacca the Wookie, returning to his family to celebrate "Life Day." The film is regularly criticised by fans and critics. Such was the embarrassment to George Lucas that this special has since all but disappeared off the face of this, and probably every other, planet.

There is a very limited amount of collectable material relating to the television special, most of it press releases and advertising material, and it is incredibly difficult to find. The show has never been released on video or DVD, and it is safe to say it never will be, so if you find someone selling copies, you can be sure they are illegal bootlegs.

▲ Star Wars Episode 1 phonecards. 1999. (ex). Sold March 2009: £19.40

▲ Return of the Jedi jigsaw puzzle. 1983. (g). Sold January 2006: £6.30

▲ Tazo Collector's Force Pack (complete). 1996. (g). Sold September 2007: £1.60

STOCK & BOND CERTIFICATES

Scripophily is the collecting and research of old cancelled stock and bond certificates.

Historically (particularly at the end of the nineteenth century), companies issued attractively printed certificates in a bid to help maximise investment. These old certificates now offer a wealth of history and are often wonderful works of art. This is a fascinating collecting area and many examples can be purchased at reasonable prices.

Generally, the tip is to look out for certificates with interesting vignettes (pictorial designs that often fade gradually at the edges). Also look for specialist subject matter such as railroad construction, telegraphy, early aviation, mining, and electric power.

The hobby has international appeal, particularly in the USA, so the internet auction route is a useful marketing vehicle.

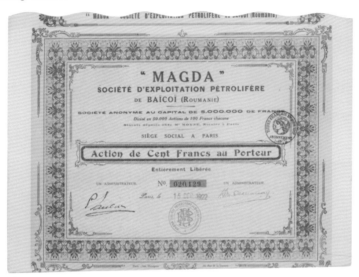

▲ Magda. 1922. (vg). Sold January 2011: £4.10

▲ The Silver Bird Cobalt Mines. 1907. (vg). Sold January 2011: £12

STOCKINGS

▲ Teena – Belmont. (1960). (ex). Sold February 2009: £5.10

▲ Elana – Dupont. (1960). (ex). Sold February 2009: £6

▲ The Avengers "Character Knit" stockings. (1965). (vg). Sold February 2008: £15.40

STYLOPHONE

The Dubreq Stylophone was invented by Brian Jarvis in 1967. It was an electronic musical instrument that made use of a stylus to complete electrical circuits that would then sound the different notes. In the UK, Rolf Harris was spokesman for the Stylophone for several years.

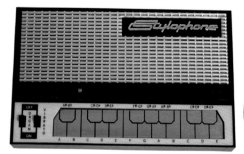

▲ Stylophone (boxed). 1970. (g-vg).Sold June 2008: £60

▲ Stylophone Latin American Album (vinyl record and book). 1970. (g).Sold September 2008: £3.10

▲ Traditional Tunes and Christmas Carols (vinyl record and book). 1970. (vg-ex). Sold January 2009: £7

▲ Rolf Harris introduces the Stylophone (vinyl record). (1970). (g-vg).Sold February 2008: £4.10

TAX DISCS (VELOLOGY)

▲ 1923 Annual. (g). Sold March 2011: £120.10

Interest in collecting expired tax discs ("velology") has been gradually increasing over the years, but the subject has only recently begun to be treated seriously.

Rare tax discs are now commanding sums between £200 and £300, and the current world record (at the time of printing) is £651.90 for a very rare March 1923 quarterly issue.

Although vehicle taxation had been in place for many years, it wasn't until the implementation of the Finance Act 1920 that the issuing and displaying of tax discs became a legal requirement, and from 1 January 1921 motorists were obliged to display a disc on the vehicle. The option was available for quarterly and annual discs.

Originally, the discs had no perforations to separate them from the outer margins (selvedge), and as a result early discs were often poorly cut out. Any disc with selvedge still attached, but particularly these early ones, are more valuable to a collector.

▲ Feb 1972 emergency issue. (f). Sold March 2011: £26.20

In 1923 rules were changed so that expired tax discs had to be destroyed. As a result, it can be harder to find discs dating from this period.

Interesting discs to watch out for include those from 1925 with advertising on the reverse, those allocated to agricultural machines (known as farmers discs), emergency discs issued when normal discs became restricted, and Welsh or Northern Ireland issues.

▲ Mar 1948 Quarterly (selvedge). (g). Sold April 2011: £21.30

▲ 1921 Annual. (f-g). Sold November 2010: £160.20

▲ Mar 1926 Quarterly (selvedge). (g). Sold November 2010: £248.10

▲ Mar 1923 Quarterly. (f). Sold November 2010: £651.90

▲ Sep 1922. (g). Sold September 2010: £526.20

▲ Feb 1972 emergency issue. (f-g). Sold September 2010: £30.10

▲ Apr 1981 (Welsh). (f). Sold
September 2010: £16.20

▲ Aug 1993 (Northern Ireland).
(g) Sold September 2010: £30.60

▲ Sep 1925 Quarterly. (f-g).
Sold July 2010: £325.90

▲ Jun 1932 Quarterly. (g-vg),
Sold July 2010: £50.30

▲ Dec 1974 trade plate. (f).
Sold July 2010: £7.10

▲ Jun 1921 Quarterly. (f). Sold
June 2010: £365.10

▲ Mar 1946 Quarterly. (g-vg).
Sold May 2010: £51.10

▲ 1958 Annual. (f-g). Sold May
2010: £16.20

▲ 1958 Annual (farmers). (f-g).
Sold April 2010: £15.10

▲ 1933 Annual. (vg). Sold
March 2010: £25.30

▲ Dec 1922 Quarterly. (f). Sold
March 2010: £100.10

▲ 1941 Annual. (vg-ex). Sold
March 2010: £22.10

TELEGRAMS

▲ Greetings telegram. 1939. (g).
Sold July 2007: £4.20

▲ Greetings telegram. 1942. (g).
Sold September 2006: £4.10

▲ Telegram. 1943. (f-g). Sold February 2008: £5.10

As with most items of ephemera, one of the most important aspects of a telegram is the content. A telegram simply wishing the recipient a happy birthday will generally be considered of far less interest than a telegram advising the recipient that the sender is about to be shipped out to a war zone.

TELEPHONES

▲ AEP telephone. 1961. (g). Sold January 2009: £38

▲ Chameleon telephone. (2000). (g). Sold June 2007: £50.10

▲ Mickey Mouse telephone. (2000). (vg). Sold July 2005: £27.20

TENNIS

◀ Adidas wooden racket. (1975). (ex). Sold July 2007: £6.60

▶ Adidas wooden racket. (1970). (vg-ex). Sold March 2008: £4.10

▲ World Champions of Tennis postcard. 1984. (vg). Sold May 2008: £7

▲ Know the Game – Short Tennis (book). 1986. (vg). Sold March 2011: £1.60

TETLEY TEA

Over the years, Tetley has teamed up with some big-name companies to produce wonderful collectables. The biggest of these companies is arguably Wade.

Wade has been making Tetley merchandise since the 1980s, and in 2006, the gift pieces for the International Wade Collectors Club were two Tea Folk Whimsies. The Wade merchandise is all masterfully made, as one would expect, and makes for some of the most handsome collectables in the vast

▲ Ceramic tea pot. 1987. (vg). Sold June 2007: £16.60

array of Tetley memorabilia. Some pieces are more valuable than others, with the most interesting examples including a tea caddy in the shape of a van (which can be expected to realise a price in excess of £20) and an incredibly rare gold-trimmed Morris Minor money box, released in September 2006, which had a limited production run of just 50 pieces and can sell for as much as £200 on the secondary market.

Another company that Tetley have teamed up with on numerous occasions is Lledo, the people responsible for the Days Gone die-cast vehicles.

MEET THE FOLK

Here are the people who are always looking forward to break time (so much so they always seemed to be in their slippers).

Gaffer
The "Doc" of the Tetley crew. Was voiced in the television adverts by talented British actor Brian Glover until his death in 1997.

Sydney
An unofficial "right hand man". A little dopey, and quite often making mistakes, but always first to get the kettle on.

Gordon
Like all the Tea Folk, Gordon's first passion is a nice cuppa, but he is also a keen gardener.

Maurice
The resident "fix-it" man with a pencil permanently stuck behind his ear. When he's puzzling over how to complete his latest invention, it's no surprise that a cup of tea is always on the cards.

Tina (Teana)
The only girl in the mix. Always ready with biscuits and cakes; the perfect tea time treats!

Clarence
Tina's boyfriend. He's young and hip, and loves music (but, of course, not as much as he loves tea).

Archie
Quite often referred to simply as "Nephew", Archie is the youngest member of the team. He doesn't actually work for Tetley, he's still at school, but he enjoys visiting and having a brew with everyone else.

▲ Tetley Tea Folk music stars premiums. 1995. (vg). Sold June 2007: £10.10

▲ Ceramic cookie jar. 1999. (vg). Sold June 2007: £15

▲ Tetley 1932 Dennis Delivery Van diecast model (Lledo). (1995). Sold June 2008: £13.50

▲ Jigsaw. (1985). (vg). Sold November 2007: £2.10

▲ Tetley 1950 Morris Z Van diecast model (Lledo). 1998. (ex). Sold September 2008: £15.10

THEATRE

Collecting theatre programmes is arguably one of the most interesting elements of theatrical memorabilia.

Some collectors look for programmes from theatres that no longer exist. They also look for star names, and sadly there's often more interest in stars who are deceased.

Values are enhanced if a programme is autographed by cast members and includes a ticket.

A good place to find old programmes is a collector's fair, where they can sometimes be bought in bulk. Auction houses are also strong hunting grounds. If you are simply buying to re-sell then finding the right buyer for the right programme can often prove a challenge.

Modern programmes are well worth collecting and if you visit the theatre, make sure you buy a programme (or two) and spend that extra little time to wait at the stage door to get it autographed. You will often have a readily saleable commodity (assuming the autographs are well known names), and could double your investment in the programme.

Other items to look out for include theatre tickets, flyers, posters, and commemorative or first day covers.

▲ The Sound of Music (preview). 1961. (vg). Sold November 2010: £20

▲ The Devil's Disciple. 1956. (g). Sold June 2010: £7.10

▲ My Fair Lady. 1958. (vg). Sold May 2010: £5.10

▲ Jack and the Beanstalk. 1948. (g-vg). Sold February 2008: £7.10

▲ George and Margaret. 1944. (g). Sold February 2008: £6.10

▲ The Talk of the Town. 1965. (vg). Sold March 2011: £4.10

▲ Shakespeare's Globe Theatre first day cover. 1995. (ex). Sold August 2008: £15.10

THIMBLES

Thimbles are protective shields worn on the finger or thumb often used while sewing. The earliest known example is a Roman thimble, found in Pompeii, that dates back to the first century AD. Collecting thimbles is now a common hobby, and collectors are often referred to as digitabulists.

▲ BA Concord. 1977. (vg).
Sold November 2010: £5

▲ Butlin's Holidays. (1980).
(vg). Sold November 2010: £3

▲ The National Lottery. (1995).
(vg). Sold November 2010: £7.10

▲ London bus. (1980).
(vg). Sold November 2010: £3

Thimbles have been popular collectables for decades and consequently have been used as marketing tools to promote seaside resorts and commerce. Some even commemorate particular events such as royal coronations.

They are ideal to buy and sell as they take up little space, they are light to post (although good packaging is essential), and they don't break the bank.

Another plus factor is that thimbles often have dual collecting value (such as the examples on this page for British Airways Concord and Butlin's Holidays).

Look out for them at car boot sales; you have a good chance of finding little gems in boxes of 'junk.'

▲ 22nd Olympiad –
Moscow. 1980. (vg). Sold
November 2010: £3

▲ VE Day. 1995. (ex)
SP £3 (25958). Sold
November 2010: £3

▲ Daily Telegraph – 10 years
of Margaret Thatcher. (vg).
Sold November 2010: £3.20

▲ Newton Abbot. (1980).
(vg). Sold November
2010: £1

▲ Isle of Man. (1980).
(vg). Sold November
2010: £5.10

▲ Dome 2000. 2000.
(vg). Sold November
2010: £5.10

TICKETS

▲ Gerry and the Pacemakers concert ticket. 8 Feb 1964. (g-vg). Sold January 2010: £13

▲ FA Cup Final Tie ticket. 1 May 1965. (g-vg). Sold May 2008: £25

▲ Judas Priest concert ticket. 22 Nov 1981. (g). Sold January 2011: £3.60

▲ Cinderella on Ice ticket. 16 Jan 1957. (g). Sold February 2011: £1

▲ Dexy's Midnight Runners concert ticket. 11 Nov 1985. (g-vg). Sold February 2011: £3.60

▲ Royal Tournament ticket. 1985. (f). Sold November 2008: £3.10

▲ National Lottery first draw ticket. 19 Nov 1994. (vg). Sold February 2011: £2

▲ Billy Smart's Circus seat ticket. 11 May 1967. (f-g). Sold February 2011: £2.10

▲ Ry Cooder concert ticket. 30 Jan 1977. (g-vg). Sold March 2011: £4.70

▲ London Transport Charles and Diana commemorative ticket. 29 Jul 1981. (vg). Sold February 2008: £4.60

▲ British Railways 2nd class season ticket. 1970. (g). Sold April 2011: £2.10

▲ Liverpool to Birkenhead 2nd class railway ticket. 1962. (g). Sold April 2011: £2.10

▲ Cornwall v Durham County Championship Final rugby ticket. 1 Apr 1989. (vg-ex). Sold March 2009: £0.20

▲ Britannia Airways ticket. 1967. (vg). Sold March 2009: £2

▲ The Sound of Music (preview) ticket. 17 May 1961. (ex). Sold November 2010: £10

▲ Channel Airways ticket. 1971. (vg). Sold February 2011: £3.60

▲ Nationwide Football League Division One Play-Off Final ticket. 12 May 2002. (g). Sold June 2008: £2

▲ Eastern Counties bus ticket. (1965). (vg). Sold February 2008: £0.10

▲ Hants & Dorset bus ticket. (1965). (f-g). Sold February 2008: £1.70

▲ England v France rugby ticket. 20 Apr 1974. (f-g). Sold November 2007: £3.60

TINS

▲ Castrol Oil tin. (1970). (g).
Sold November 2010: £5.10

Try to display your tins out of direct sunlight, which can otherwise cause fading. Do not be tempted to clean up or restore tins, and at most give them a light dusting with a cloth when necessary. The best advice is to leave them alone! If you have a very dirty example that you just have to clean with soap and water, make sure the tin is left to dry for at least 24 hours before closing the lid and displaying it. Any damp will promote rusting, and rusting will cause more harm to the value (and appearance) of a collection than anything else.

If you are collecting for fun rather than as an investment, then you may decide to collect modern rather than vintage tins. Modern tins can be bought for little expense, and you will quickly be able to build up a large and colourful collection which you can enjoy for many years to come. Of course, these are the vintage tins of the future, and who can tell how prices of such items will increase?

It can be quite difficult to spot reproduction or fake tins, but there are some basic guidelines to help. Remember that it is very unlikely that you will find a mint condition tin with really bright paintwork. Genuine old tins are likely to have faded, and there will probably be some evidence of wear or rust. Furthermore, genuine vintage tins will tend to be heavier than the new reproductions.

A good tip is to look out for people selling items in old tins, where the items are being sold for less than the value of the tins they are in. This happens time and again at car boot sales.

▲ J Grunebaum & Sons cigarette tin.
(1920). (f). Sold June 2010: £20.10

A popular brand is Huntley & Palmers. The company was founded in 1822 by Joseph Huntley. In 1868 the company received a royal warrant and to celebrate they launched a transfer printed tin. This proved so popular that they produced many more and towards the end of the nineteenth century they took advantage of the new technology of lithographic printing.

As well as attractive rectangular tins, the company became much more adventurous and began producing tins in various shapes. In fact there were around 400 different designs. These included bells, binocular cases, lanterns, vases and many more. Values can run into hundreds of pounds for well preserved examples.

The best place to find them is at a collectors' fair. Internet purchases don't offer the opportunity to examine the tin carefully before buying. Some of the more desirable examples include those shaped like books, vans, trains, or teapots.

▲ Huntley & Palmers casket biscuit tin. 1913. (f-g). Sold February 2009: £25

▲ Huntley & Palmers handbag biscuit tin. 1904. (f). Sold February 2009: £5.60

▲ Independent Order of Rechabites Centenary tin. 1935. (f-g). Sold September 2010: £10.10

▲ Bergamottes de Nancy tin. (1925). (f-g). Sold June 2011: £4.20

▲ Tom Thumb cigars tin. (1955). (g-vg). Sold September 2010: £2.60

▲ Pascall Creme de Menthe. (1920). (f-g). Sold June 2011: £5.20

▲ Romac Junior repair outfit tin. (1950). (g). Sold May 2010: £6

▲ Elephant mathematical instruments tin. (1960). (g). Sold May 2010: £3.20

▲ Coleman's Mustard tin. (1935). (g). Sold May 2010: £3.20

▲ Oxo coronation tin. 1953. (vg). Sold January 2010: £10.10

▲ Tan Floro wax polish tin. (1935). (g). Sold March 2010: £3

▲ Kleen-e-ze wax polish tin. (1950). (g-vg). Sold March 2010: £6.10

▲ Sellotape tin. (1965). (g). Sold March 2010: £6.10

▲ Dome topped drawing pins tin. (1920). (p). Sold March 2010: £3.20

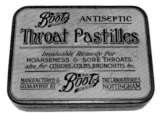

▲ Boots Throat Pastilles tin. (1925). (g). Sold January 2010: £4.30

▲ Meggezones tin. (1960). (g). Sold January 2010: £3.20

▲ Meloids tin. (1935). (g). Sold January 2010: £5.10

▲ Huntley & Palmers biscuit tin. (1925). (g). Sold March 2010: £10.30

▲ Kiwi wax floor polish tin. (1960). (vg). Sold January 2010: £3

▲ Huntley & Palmers Ancient Lock biscuit tin. 1896. (g). Sold March 2009: £7.50

▲ Snow White toffee tin. (1955). (g-vg). Sold June 2005: £12.10

▲ John Bell's Cold Capsules tin. (1940). (g). Sold June 2006: £7.40

▲ Huntley & Palmers biscuit tin. (1925). (g). Sold June 2008: £5

▲ Casco casein glue tin. (1955). (g). Sold June 2008: £3.80

▲ Harry Potter sweets tin. 1999. (vg). Sold June 2008: £1.50

TOBACCIANA

Tobacciana is the term used for items relating to tobacco companies. It's a huge subject with hundreds of different companies involved, many of which are no longer in existence. You could consider collecting items relating to a particular brand in order to focus your collection to a more manageable size.

▲ Player's Please glass sign. (1950). 350 x 240mm. (vg). Sold May 2009: £12

▲ Kensitas tin advertising sign. (1950). 512 x 170mm. (g). Sold June 2007: £40.10

▲ Kensitas packet of four. (1930). (f). Sold June 2007: £4.90

▲ Player's No.6 metal advertising sign. (1965). 395 x 184mm. (g). Sold February 2009: £15.50

◀ Player's Navy Cut tin. (1950). (g). Sold March 2010: £10.20

▲ Nelson hardboard advertising sign. (1950). 760 x 510mm. (g). Sold May 2009: £45

▲ Woodbine glass ash tray. (1970). (vg). Sold April 2008: £14.60

▲ Embassy live (complete and un-opened) cigarette packet. (1965). (ex). Sold January 2011: £15

▲ State Express 777 cigarette tin. (1950). (g). Sold February 2011: £5.10

▲ Bristol playing cards. (1950). (ex). Sold February 2009: £15

▲ Bulwark Cut Plug tobacco tin. (1935). (g). Sold March 2010: £6.10

▲ Benson & Hedges BOAC tin. (1960). (g-vg). Sold March 2010: £5.20

▲ The "Greys" silk cut tin. (1925). (g-vg). Sold August 2010: £3.10

▲ Wills's OK Flake tin. (1935). (p-f). Sold March 2010: £6.10

▲ Hamlet (VHS video). (1990). (vg). Sold September 2008: £1.20

▲ Prince Albert Crimp Cut tin. (1910). (f-g). Sold June 2010: £6.10

▲ Marlboro ceramic ash tray. (1990). (g-vg). Sold April 2008: £10

▲ Capstan ceramic ash tray. (1965). (vg). Sold May 2009: £21

▲ Silk Cut ceramic ash tray. (1985). (vg). Sold January 2010: £5.10

▲ Gold Flake coronation tin. 1937. (f). Sold March 2010: £10.60

▲ Gold Flake Honey Dew tin. (1950). (f). Sold March 2010: £10.20

▲ Wills's Gold Flake playing cards. (1950). (g-vg).Sold February 2009: £10.10

▲ Senior Service tin. (1950). (f). Sold March 2010: £10.10

▲ Senior Service cigarette tin. (1950). (f). Sold February 2008: £6

▲ Senior Service glass jug. (1960). (vg). Sold February 2008: £12.50

▲ Senior Service swizzle stick. (1965). (vg).Sold February 2008: £5

▲ Robin cigarettes pub board game. (1935). (f). Sold January 2010: £28.10

TOFFEE HAMMERS

▲ William's toffee hammer. (1930). (g). Sold September 2009: £6.10

▲ McCowans toffee hammer. (2000). (g). Sold February 2008: £3

▲ Blue Bird toffee hammer. (1990). (g). Sold February 2008: £1

▲ Sharps toffee hammer. (1960). (g). Sold February 2008: £3.10

▲ Small Sharps toffee hammer. (1965). (g). Sold October 2007: £8

▲ Walkers toffee hammer. (1970). (g).Sold July 2005: £4

TOOLS

▲ Majestic All-Purpose Sharpener. 1972. (g-vg). Sold July 2007: £2

▲ Autoflex steel tape rule. (1970). (vg). Sold September 2007: £3

▲ Set square. (1950). (g). Sold May 2005: £3

▲ Rolson block plane. (1970). (g). Sold February 2005: £5

▲ Dolls house furniture. (1980). (g). Sold November 2010: £4.40

▲ Lullaby Mother tinplate mechanical toy. (1955). (vg). Sold May 2010: £40.10

▲ Wooden horse. (1950). (g). Sold July 2007: £10

▲ Tinplate kaleidoscope. (1965). (g). Sold September 2007: £11.20

▲ Typewriter xylophone. (1960). (g-vg). Sold July 2010: £9.70

▲ Petite Playmates rag doll. (1990). (vg-ex). Sold January 2010: £3.60

▲ Garfield diecast model (ERTL). (1990). (mnt). Sold July 2007: £5.10

▲ Mercedes Grand Prix tinplate clockwork car. 1990. (vg). Sold April 2011: £25.70

▲ Tinplate racing car. (1965). (f-g). Sold August 2007: £10.10

▲ Scalextric Tri-ang green BRM. (1965). (g). Sold July 2007: £5

▲ Huckleberry Hound Roll-A-Ball game. (1960). (f). Sold January 2008: £10.80

▲ Cup Final bagatelle. (1960). (g-vg). Sold July 2007: £15

▲ Wheel of Fortune bagatelle. (1965). (g). Sold June 2007: £6

▲ Timpo 6 shooter. (1970). (g-vg). Sold April 2010: £16

▲ Wild West Spin Dart game. (1950). (vg). Sold August 2007: £24.40

▲ The Fulton Great American Printer. (1925). (f). Sold April 2010: £18.70

▲ Wizard electronic game. 1987. (ex). Sold July 2007: £7

▲ Tinplate spinning top. (1950). (g-vg). Sold October 2007: £21

▲ Boxwood toy soldiers. (1970). (f-g). Sold August 2007: £8.10

▲ Tinplate GTP 580 Pleasure Launch. (1965). (g-vg). Sold September 2007: £10.30

TRADING STAMPS

▲ Green Shield Stamps saver book. (1975). (g). Sold May 2007: £3.80

Trading stamps were a type of loyalty promotion first introduced in the United States in 1896. They became very popular throughout the early to mid 1900s, and in 1958 they were introduced in the UK when Richard Tompkins founded the Green Shield Trading Stamp Co. Rival schemes included S&H Pink Stamps and the Co-op dividend stamps.

Stamps were acquired for spending fixed amounts in store, and were then collected into books which could be exchanged for products from a catalogue. Tesco was one of the largest companies to take part in the Green Shield scheme.

Individual stamps are now collectable, and complete books are desirable; however, there is not a huge market for the stamps and at the moment they are not likely to realise huge sums at auction.

▲ Co-op stamp book. (1975). (g). Sold May 2007: £1

▲ S&H Pink Stamps saver book. (1975). (g-vg). Sold February 2008: £2

▲ Green Shield Stamps information leaflet. (1960). (vg). Sold September 2008: £1.30

TREEN

Treen is a very specific term for small, functional items made of wood. Items of furniture are not classed as treen because they are too large, and ornaments are not classed as treen because they do not have a function. Examples of treen include spoons, plates, shoe horns, and chopping boards.

▲ Tie press. (1935). (g). Sold August 2008: £7.10

▲ Catapult. (1970). (g). Sold April 2008: £4.20

▲ Nut cracker. (1925). (g). Sold June 2007: £7.10

▲ Church collection box. (1935). (vg). Sold March 2010: £33.80

TV AND RADIO LICENCES

When the Government decided to start a national radio service in 1922, they called it the British Broadcasting Corporation (BBC). It was funded by a General Post Office (GPO) receiving licence under the statute of the Wireless Telegraph Act.

The cost of the first wireless (radio) licence was 10/- (50p), and today that same licence in good condition will command a minimum of 20 times the original cost.

In 1946 the cost of a radio licence increased from 10/- to £1 and at the same time a new licence was launched to fund the BBC television service. This new broadcast receiving TV licence cost £2 but incorporated the cost of radio.

Early combined (TV and radio) licences are quite hard to find because television was yet to become affordable to the masses.

The market for TV and radio licences is in its infancy and traders/collectors will ultimately decide whether or not values will significantly increase.

▲ Colour licence. Issued March 1993. C10 stamp. (g). Sold March 2010: £0.60

▲ Colour TV licence. Issued March 1990. C7 stamp. (g). Sold March 2010: £0.60

▲ Colour licence. Issued July 1988. C6 stamp. (vg). Sold March 2010: £0.70

▲ Colour TV licence. Issued March 1989. C6 stamp. (vg). Sold March 2010: £0.70

▲ Colour licence. Issued April 1977. £18 stamp. (g). Sold March 2010: £1.10

▲ Colour TV licence. Issued September 1981. C3 stamp. (g). Sold March 2010: £0.70

TV SHOWS

▲ World of Sport annual. 1978. (vg). Sold March 2011: £3.90

▲ Stingray annual. 1993. (g). Sold March 2010: £2.20

▲ Thank Your Luck Stars (hardback book). 1964. (g-vg). Sold August 2010: £10

▲ Buck Rogers starfighter diecast model (Corgi). 1980-83. (vg). Sold September 2010: £10

▲ Coronation Street: The Album (vinyl LP). 1987. Vinyl (vg), sleeve (vg). Sold February 2011: £5.10

▲ The Avengers: Parallel Lines Volume 6 (VHS video). 1998. (vg). Sold July 2010: £5.10

▲ Theme from Z Cars (vinyl single). 1962. Vinyl (g), repro sleeve (mnt). Sold January 2010: £12.10

▲ Z Cars Ford Zephyr 6 MKIII diecast model (Corgi). 2000. (ex-mnt). Sold January 2010: £15.10

▲ The Prisoner: Episodes 1 & 2 (VHS video). 1986. (vg). Sold February 2011: £2.40

▲ Archie Andrews annual (no.5). (1955). (g-vg). Sold March 2010: £25.10

▲ Heartbeat North Riding police van diecast model (Lledo). 1998. (mnt). Sold March 2011: £6.60

TV STARS

When building a collection relating to a specific television actor, the star's autograph is obviously one of the most desirable items to acquire. Publicity photographs, books (particularly autobiographies), and even magazines where the star features on the cover will also make good additions.

▲ Johnny Morris signed commemorative cover. (vg). Sold June 2011: £25.10

▲ In the Flower Garden with Percy Thrower (book). 1957. (g). Sold February 2011: £3.80

▲ Dickie Davies autograph. Dedicated. Sold March 2011: £10

▲ Patrick McGoohan publicity photograph (pre-printed signature). (1965). (g). Sold February 2011: £3.10

▲ Warren Mitchell signed photograph. No dedication. Sold February 2011: £10.10

▲ Little Britain autographs. No dedications. Sold January 2011: £10

▲ Jon Pertwee (Worzel Gummidge) publicity photograph (pre-printed signature). (1980). (g). Sold November 2010: £5.10

▲ Leonard Rossiter signed photograph. No dedication. Sold August 2010: £50.10

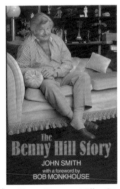

▲ The Benny Hill Story (hardback book). 1988. (vg). Sold November 2010: £5.10

TYPEWRITER RIBBON TINS

The very first typewriter (circa 1870) required the use of an inked ribbon through which type struck the paper. Approximately 20 years later, tins were used as containers for the ribbons. Tins were eventually replaced by plastic containers in the early 1970s.

Collectors look for colourful, artistic designs and they have thousands to choose from, from all parts of the world.

Look out for some really good examples at Collectors' Fairs, quite often reasonably priced. However, some of the best sources are internet auctions.

▲ Imperitype tin (with ribbon). (1955). (vg). Sold March 2011: £5

▲ Imperitype tin (empty). (1935). (g-vg). Sold March 2011: £4

▲ Kee Lox tin (empty). (1946). (vg). Sold March 2011: £4

▲ Woodwards' tin (with ribbon). (1935). (g-vg). Sold March 2011: £6.60

▲ Pyro tin (empty). (1935). (g). Sold May 2008: £6.10

▲ Cora tin (empty). (1945). (f). Sold February 2008: £2.10

VALENTINE CARDS

Saint Valentine's Day is held every 14 February. It is a celebration of love, named after a number of Christian martyrs, which was first established by Pope Gelasius I in 496 AD.

Interestingly, there was originally no connection between the day and romance, and the first recorded association of Valentine's Day with love is in Parlement of Foules, a poem written by Geoffrey Chaucer in 1382 to honour the anniversary of the engagement of King Richard II to Anne of Bohemia.

▲ "To my Valentine." (1910). (vg-ex). Sold September 2009: £5.10

▲ Heart-shaped. (1940). (f). Sold June 2007: £3.20

▲ Valentine postcard. (1910). (g) Sold June 2009: £5

A young Frenchman, Charles, Duke of Orleans, was one of the earliest creators of valentines, called "poetical or amorous addresses." From his confinement in the Tower of London after the Battle of Agincourt in 1415, he sent several poems or rhymed love letters or "Valentines" to his wife in France.

The first commercial Valentine did not appear until about 1800, but they quickly became very popular in England and were soon being assembled en masse in factories. These early Valentines were made with real lace and ribbons and are obviously very desirable among collectors.

As well as very old cards, collectors will also be interested in unusual or novelty cards, such as those cut into shapes or those with moving parts. Cards with illustrations by famous artists are also popular.

▲ "With love to my wife." (1950). (f). Sold September 2007: £0.30

VIEW-MASTER

The View-Master was released in 1938, born from a partnership between William Gruber and Harold Graves of Sawyers Photographic Services. The device was originally intended to be an educational tool for young children, but it quickly became a popular form of entertainment. Some of the most popular series of reels for collectors today involve Disney characters, but Sawyers did not acquire the rights to these characters until 1951, after they had purchased rival company Tru-Vue.

In 1966, Sawyer's was acquired by the General Aniline & Film Corporation, and from then on View-Master products carried "gaf" branding.

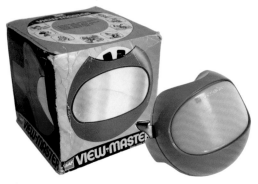

There's a lot to the subject of collecting View-Master. You can collect viewers, projectors, reels, books, containers, and more. The demand is out there and consequently there's normally a willing buyer for any related products.

Always watch out for items at car boot sales. You may accidentally pick up a rare variation that a seasoned collector will pay way over the odds for. Furthermore, many people are completely unaware of the existence of a buoyant market and just about anything can be bought below its true value.

▲ GAF Model K viewer. (1975). (vg). Sold August 2009: £20

▲ Madame Tussauds picture reels. (1965). (vg-ex). Sold November 2010: £10

▲ Tom & Jerry picture reels. (1968). (vg). Sold March 2010: £8.30

▲ The Magic Roundabout picture reels. 1966. (g-vg). Sold February 2009: £5.10

▲ Hong Kong picture reels. (1965). (vg). Sold September 2009: £6

▲ Australia picture reels. (1970). (vg). Sold September 2009: £3.70

▲ History of Flight. 1973. (vg). Sold June 2009: £20.50

▲ Disney's 101 Dalmatians View-Master set. 1996. (g). Sold April 2008: £19.90

▲ Cabbage Patch Kids View-Master set. 1984. (vg). Sold March 2008: £17

▲ Fairy Tales gift pack (Model G viewer and 7 reels). (1968). (vg). Sold May 2010: £28.80

▲ Light attachment. (1955). (g). Sold March 2008: £25.10

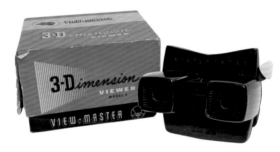

▲ Model E viewer. (1955). (vg). Sold December 2008: £20.60

▲ UFO picture reels. 1969. (vg). Sold May 2008: £13.50

▲ Picture reel album. (1957). (vg). Sold January 2008: £10.10

WADE

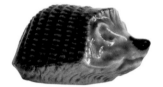

▲ Hedgehog. 1967. (vg). Sold July 2008: £8

▲ Chimp Boy with Teapot Whimsie. 1978. (ex). Sold July 2008: £7.10

Originally, Wade Ceramics Ltd was made up of three different companies run by Wade family members, the earliest of which was established in 1867. The companies combined under the name Wade Potteries Ltd in 1958, and the name was changed to Wade Ceramics Ltd in 1998.

Over the years, Wade has produced various items that have become collectors' items. Many of their products are produced under licence, so as well as being collectable in their own right they can also be nice additions to themed collections.

Wade Whimsies are quite popular, although they remain relatively inexpensive at the moment. They first appeared in 1953 after Wade potteries lost contracts in their traditional industrial ceramics market. Ten sets were produced up until 1959 and then Wade stopped general production, but continued manufacturing Whimsies as promotional items given away with various products such as tea bags.

In 1971 Wade began to market the Whimsies as a retail line again. 12 sets were produced up until 1980 and production continued until 1984.

▲ Hippo Whimsie. 1973. (g). Sold September 2009: £4.30

▲ Elephant Whimsie. 1973. (g). Sold July 2008: £5

▲ Flintstones dinosaur. 1965. (vg). Sold August 2008: £8.10

▲ Angel Fish. 1978. (vg). Sold July 2008: £11.50

▲ Beaver. 1972. (vg). Sold September 2009: £3.30

▲ Sea Lion Whimsie. 1984. (vg). Sold July 2008: £10

Wade also produced a series of pig moneyboxes for NatWest Bank in 1983 (taking over from Sunshine Ceramics who originally made the pigs in 1982). This was to give youngsters an incentive to save. As a child's balance grew, they were able to increase their collection of pigs.

A child received their first pig (Woody, the baby) when they saved £1 and they received the final pig in the collection (Sir Nathaniel Westminster, the father) when they saved £100. Lady Hillary (the mother), Maxwell (the boy) and Annabel (the girl) were the other pigs in the collection. The offer ended in 1988. In 1998, NatWest added Cousin Wesley to the series.

Thousands of the pigs were made but relatively few children managed to complete the set. £100 was a large sum of money for a young saver then.

Cousin Wesley was limited to only 5,000 and it was given away when a child took out a 5 year investment of £1000. Therefore, due to its limited availability, Cousin Wesley is now the most valuable pig to own (although beware of the fakes that have recently flooded the market).

◀ Hilary Natwest pig. 1983. (vg). Sold May 2008: £27.10

◀ Sir Nathanial Westminster pig. 1983. (vg). Sold June 2008: £75

◀ Woody pig. 1983. (g-vg). Sold September 2009: £10.50

▲ Fake Cousin Wesley

Spotting a Fake Cousin Wesley

It is very difficult to spot a fake Cousin Wesley, but knowing as many details as possible about a genuine example will help you spot the fakes when they turn up. Even if the example you are looking at matches all of the below criteria, there is still no guarantee it is genuine.

- Height should be 146mm

- Width of base should be no more than 102mm

- Weight should be 371gms

- Shirt should be green, hat and trousers should be blue

- Inside should be white (no glazing)

WEDGWOOD

The first Wedgwood factory was founded in 1759 by Josiah Wedgwood, who is now commonly referred to as the father of English potters because of his ground-breaking innovations. Three of the ceramic styles that the Wedgwood potters are still well-known for today were invented by Josiah himself, namely Queen's Ware (in 1762), Black Basalt (in 1768), and Jasper (in 1774). That these styles remain so enduringly popular is testament to Josiah's exemplary skill and eye for beauty.

▲ Wild Strawberry vase. (1965). (vg). Sold March 2006: £12.20

Queen's Ware is a cream-coloured earthenware. It is named after Queen Charlotte, the wife of George III, who was presented with a tea set by Josiah in 1765 and was so delighted that she allowed it to be called Queen's Ware, guaranteeing its popularity across the country. Josiah was also appointed Potter to Her Majesty, and with such a grand history of Royal associations it is no surprise that ever since Wedgwood has been a frontrunner in producing souvenirs, such as mugs and plates, to commemorate major Royal events.

Black Basalt allowed Josiah to produce replicas of Etruscan pottery from Italy. The products were beautifully crafted with smooth, purple-black surfaces, and they were another huge success story. However, arguably the most-loved of Josiah's innovations was Jasper Ware: blue, unglazed ceramics with white bass-relief. Interestingly, Jasper can be any colour, but blue with white relief is the most common and most desirable. Even more interestingly, the way in which Jasper is made today is almost exactly the same as when Josiah first invented it all those years ago.

▲ New Year bell. 1979. (vg). Sold June 2007: £9.70

Almost all Wedgwood items are stamped with the Wedgwood name, and it would pay for a collector to study the different stamps used over the years to get a better understanding of when items were made (and whether or not they are even genuine Wedgwood merchandise).

WINNIE THE POOH

▲ Royal Doulton ceramic statue (Pooh Counting the Honey Pots). 1997. (vg). Sold May 2008: £35

▲ Plastic money box. (1990). (g). Sold July 2008: £4.10

▲ Royal Doulton ceramic statue (Pooh Began to Eat). 2000. (vg). Sold September 2006: £60

WORLD CUP 1966

The eighth staging of the World Cup was held in England throughout July of 1966. England had been chosen as hosts by FIFA in August 1960 as a celebration of the centenary of the standardisation of football in England.

In total, 70 nations took part, and it would have been even more if 16 African nations hadn't boycotted the tournament in protest of a controversial FIFA ruling that meant teams from Africa, Asia, and Australia would all need to fight it out for just a single place in the finals.

England eventually won the tournament, beating West Germany, 4-2, in the final and becoming the first host nation to win since Italy in 1934. Three of England's goals were scored by Geoff Hurst (the only player to have ever scored a hat trick in a World Cup final) and one was scored by Martin Peters.

Of course, the final moments of the competition have gone down in footballing history. The game had gone into extra time, when Hurst scored his second goal, making the score 3-2. With seconds left on the clock, fans invaded the pitch, and BBC commentator Kenneth Wolstenholme declared, "Some people are on the pitch. They think it's all over..." At that exact moment, Hurst found the back of the net once again, making the score 4-2, and Wolstenholme cried, "It is now!"

▲ 1966 World Cup Final (VHS video). 1996. (ex). Sold April 2010: £5.10

▲ World Cup 1966 First Day Cover. 1 June 1966. (vg). Sold April 2010: £10.20

1966 World Cup Final Programme

An original in excellent condition would be worth £150 - £180. A fake is worth almost nothing. So make sure you do not get conned into buying a fake for £180!

The original programme weighs 130g. Although, at a boot sale or a collectors' fair, you are unlikely to be carrying around a set of scales, so you need to look out for the following things to avoid buying a fake:

The original programme was printed in two stages. The outer section was printed first. After the finalists were known, the inner section was printed. There was a slight discrepancy in paper quality (the inside pages are slightly darker than the outer pages) which is clearly visible when you look at the programme from the side. The vast majority of reprints/fakes will only have one colour throughout the publication.

The cigarette advert on page 2 originally had a two tone effect, which is missing from many reprints.

The cigarette advert on the back page had a definite red tinge on the original, whereas many of the reprints have a clear orange tinge.

Just by looking at the front cover, there are a couple of things to check:

The original had a definite blue tint to the "England v West Germany" text, whereas a lot of the reprints are clearly black.

On many reprints, there is a trace of white around the word "Final". This was not on the original.

▲ Trench warfare (postcard). 1915. (g-vg). Sold February 2011: £3.10

▲ "Something in a uniform" (postcard). 1916. (vg). Sold March 2010: £4.90

▲ British soldiers (postcard). 1917. (g-vg). Sold May 2006: £10

▲ The War Budget. 26 Aug 1915. (g). Sold August 2007: £4

▲ Tommy and Jack's Reward (poem on card). (1918). (g). Sold May 2008: £20

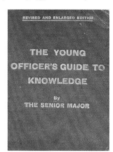

▲ Soldier dispersal certificate. 1919. (g). Sold July 2007: £10.60

▲ Young Officer's Guide to Knowledge (booklet). 1915. (f). Sold February 2005: £7.70

French "silk" postcards were incredibly popular with Allied troops during the First World War. There were three main types of such cards ("woven," "printed," and "embroidered") and the most common are the embroidered ones. Surprisingly, considering the level of detail, these little works of art were made by hand.

Because of the time and effort involved to make them, these postcards were generally more expensive than normal postcards, so they tended to be reserved for special occasions such as birthdays and anniversaries. As such, the personal notes on "silk" cards tend to be rather emotional, sending messages of love from the trenches to wives, parents, and children back home.

It is thought that about 10 million embroidered postcards were produced between 1914 and 1918, but after the War their popularity declined. By 1923 hand embroidery had been replaced by machined embroidery, and the "silk" postcard had all but disappeared entirely by 1945.

▲ "Britons all" (silk postcard). 1915. (g). Sold August 2010: £7.20

▲ "Kind thoughts" (silk postcard). (1915). (f). Sold August 2010: £4.70

▲ "Ever faithful" (silk postcard). (1915). (vg). Sold August 2010: £4.70

▲ War Office official confirmation of appointment with Land Forces. 1918. (vg). Sold October 2006: £12

▲ Poppy Day Poster. 1937. (f). Sold January 2006: £5.10

▲ "On War Service" enamel lapel badge. 1914. (g). Sold July 2008: £25.50

▲ Rolls-Royce Armoured Car diecast model (Matchbox). 1990. (ex). Sold April 2008: £30.10

▲ "On War Service" badge. 1915. (g). Sold February 2009: £15.70

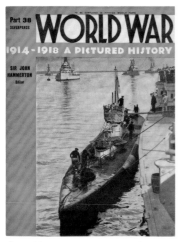

▲ World War magazine (Part 38). 1935. (g). Sold September 2009: £5.10

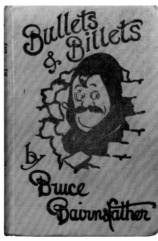

▲ Bullets and Billets (hardback book). 1916. (g). Sold March 2005: £51.10

▲ National Saving lapel badge. (1916). (vg). Sold July 2008: £9.20

▲ Old Contemptibles Association lapel badge. (1914). (vg). Sold August 2005: £22.60

▲ Dig for victory leaflet. 1945. (f). Sold May 2007: £2.30

▲ A Seaman's Pocket Book. 1945. (f). Sold May 2007: £5.10

▲ Civil Defence gas mask information leaflet. 1939. (g). Sold October 2007: £4

▲ Fruit bottling without sugar leaflet. 1944. (g). Sold August 2007: £2

▲ Civil Defence button. 1940. (g).Sold May 2007: £3

▲ Air Raid Precautions lapel badge. (1940). (g). Sold August 2007: £11

▲ Women's Institute badge. (1945). (g). Sold June 2006: £10.50

▲ 9th Army Desert Rats cloth badge. (1944). (g). Sold September 2007: £15

▲ Air Raid Precautions lamp (hand painted, with hood). (1940). (ex). Sold April 2005: £35.90

▲ Civilian First Aid for War Wounded (book). 1940. (f-g). Sold January 2008: £6.10

▲ The Aeroplane Spotter (Vol 1, No 20). 15 May 1941. (f). Sold April 2008: £5.70

▲ Aviator playing cards. 1943. (f). Sold March 2008: £11.40

▲ National Savings Certificates advertising leaflet. 1943. (vg). Sold November 2008: £10

▲ 20mm shell case. 1942. (g). Sold June 2008: £18.70

▲ Medium size respirator. 1939-1945. (vg). Sold February 2008: £25

▲ Air Raid bicycle lamp. (1940). (vg). Sold February 2008: £21

▲ Air Raid Precautions whistle. (1940). (g-vg). Sold June 2006: £13.10

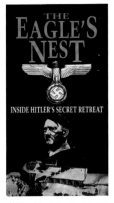

▲ RAF cloth wings. (1944). (vg). Sold October 2007: £10.10

▲ Military tailor's breakdown of costs for Black Watch uniform. 1940. (f). Sold August 2008: £12.60

▲ The Eagle's Nest (VHS video). 1994. (g). Sold March 2009: £12.20

▲ Panzer NCO and Officers breast eagle. (1940). (vg). Sold October 2007: £20

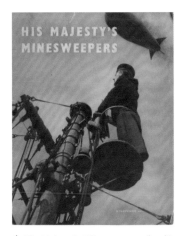

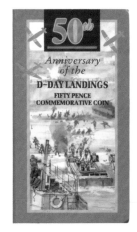

▲ His Majesty's Minesweepers (book). 1943. (g). Sold November 2010: £7.60

▲ The War Illustrated (Vol 2, No 35). 3 May 1940. (vg). Sold March 2011: £5.20

▲ D-Day commemorative 50p coin. 1994. (vg-ex). Sold March 2006: £5.20

YO-YOs

▲ Genuine Russell Professional Hyper Russell. (1990). (g). Sold September 2008: £10

▲ Pro Yo. (2000). (g). Sold May 2008: £6

▲ Stinger (real scorpion inside). (1975). (vg). Sold September 2008: £10.10

▲ Sprite. (1995). (g). Sold May 2008: £6

▲ Mickey Mouse. (1990). (vg). Sold April 2008: £4.30

▲ Gold Atom 7000 Moose's Original. (1990). (f). Sold April 2008: £7.50

▲ Basketball. (1990). (g). Sold March 2010: £3

ZOO

Old zoo guides are becoming increasingly collectable. Looking over old guides can give a fascinating insight into how attitudes towards the confinement and public exhibition of animals have changed over the years.

▲ London Zoo (postcard). (1910). (g). Sold August 2009: £5.10

▲ London Zoo Guide. 1979. (g-vg). Sold September 2007: £10

▲ Bristol Zoo key ring. (1980). (vg). Sold June 2008: £1.60

▲ Young Spotter's Guides: Zoo Animals. 1979. (p-f). Sold May 2008: £1.50

MISCELLANEOUS

▲ Geneve medal. 1925. (vg). Sold May 2011: £5.20

▲ Gordon's Gin beer mat. (1960). (vg). Sold June 2011: £4.80

▲ Friction driven UFO toy. (1965). (vg). Sold June 2011: £30.30

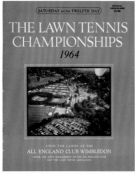

▲ Lawn Tennis Championship programme. July 1964. (g-vg). Sold June 2011: £12

▲ Pirate character jug. (1970). (vg). Sold May 2011: £5

▲ Dinky Toys catalogue (8th edition). 1960. (vg). Sold June 2011: £25.10

▲ John Smith's Bitter badge. (1990). (vg). Sold June 2011: £2.60

▲ Prince concert ticket. August 2007. (vg). Sold June 2011: £3.10

▲ Royal Opera (Covent Garden) programme. March 1939. (g-vg). Sold June 2011: £16.60

▲ Novelty guitar lighter. (2000). (vg). Sold January 2008: £5.60

▲ Army Paratroopers cloth sleeve wings. (1945). (vg). Sold June 2011: £2

MISCELLANEOUS

▲ Royal Doulton Falstaff character jug. 1960. (vg). Sold May 2011: £20.20

▲ London Underground railway map. (1945). (g). Sold June 2011: £25.20

▲ Marilyn Monroe postcard. (1950). (vg). Sold May 2011: £5.60

▲ Sprung coin holder. (1940). (vg). Sold May 2011: £14

▲ Psycho – Robert Bloch (paperback book). 1962. (g). Sold March 2011: £2.20

▲ Ever Ready Motormate light. (1965). (g). Sold March 2011: £4.60

▲ Novelty butlin's ceramic whale. (1970). (g-vg). Sold May 2011: £20.10

▲ Butlin's advertising mirror. (1960). (g-vg). Sold May 2011: £25.10

▲ AA key fob. (1980). (f). Sold March 2011: £3.60

MISCELLANEOUS

▲ John Wayne ceramic plate. (2005). (ex). Sold May 2011: £15.10

▲ James Cook pewter figure. 1979. (vg). Sold March 2011: £6.10

▲ Sefton (horse) commemorative plate. 1982. (vg). Sold April 2011: £6

▲ Jaguar car mascot. (1965). (vg). Sold April 2011: £40.10

▲ Hardwood dolly pegs. (1965). (g). Sold March 2011: £12.10

▲ Autograph of Chief Constable Ronnie Flanagan (Royal Ulster Constabulary). (vg). Sold January 2011: £11.10

▲ Bus bell push. (1960). (vg). Sold May 2011: £20.40

▲ Aluminium GB sign. (1960). (g). Sold April 2011: £15.10

▲ Band of Hope Temperance Society badge. (1950). (g). Sold June 2011: £6.30

▲ Lurpak butter dish. 2000. (g). Sold April 2011: £5

▲ Wooden football rattle. (1935). (vg). Sold September 2007: £22.30

MISCELLANEOUS

▲ The Moor's Last Sigh – Salman Rushdie (signed hardback book). Sold November 2010: £15

▲ Pocket watch with Roman coin design. (2000). (vg). Sold September 2010: £18.30

▲ Yorkshire Cricket Club Annual Report. 1962. (vg). Sold November 2010: £3.70

▲ Boomerang. (1975). (vg). Sold June 2010: £5.80

▲ Rand automatic clothes brush. (1970). (vg). Sold November 2010: £4

▲ Seraflo cloth flour bag. (1930). (vg). Sold September 2010: £10.30

▲ Royal Masonic Institution for Boys medal. 1950. (ex). Sold August 2010: £8.10

▲ BEA enamel pin badge. (1970). (vg). Sold August 2011: £5

▲ Enamel railway armband. (1960). (vg-ex). Sold July 2010: £10

▲ Radio Ulster ceramic mug. (2000). (vg). Sold September 2010: £1

▲ Brass jet fighter. (1965). (vg). Sold July 2010: £10

MISCELLANEOUS

▲ Quink Royal Blue ink. (1965). (p-f). Sold July 2010: £1

▲ Columbia record cleaner. (1925). (f). Sold June 2010: £12.70

▲ Wax tapers. (1910). (g). Sold March 2010: £10

▲ Homer Simpson tie. 1999. (ex). Sold May 2010: £4.10

▲ SS Officer toy soldier. (2000). (g). Sold July 2010: £2.10

▲ Port decanter. (1970). (vg). Sold July 2010: £3.60

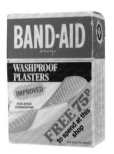

▲ Band-Aid box. 1979. (g). Sold May 2010: £2.50

▲ Daily Mail Nipper annual. 1939. (g). Sold June 2010: £5

▲ Fairy Liquid plastic bottle. (1968). (g). Sold May 2010: £10.10

▲ Kennet Council parking disc. (1971). (g). Sold May 2010: £7.80

▲ Vulcan toy sewing machine. (1960). (g). Sold March 2010: £15.60

MISCELLANEOUS

▲ Sooty xylophone. (1960). (f-g). Sold March 2010: £14.50

▲ Desmo tax disc holder. (1955). (f). Sold March 2010: £2

▲ Will Scarlett Bunnykins ceramic statue.
2002. (ex). Sold March 2010: £6.60

▲ Coalport trinket dish. (1975). (ex).
Sold March 2010: £10.10

▲ Pottery money box. (1980).
(g). Sold June 2010: £4.20

▲ KP crisps friar ceramic mug.
(1985). (g). Sold March 2010: £4

▲ Kansas City Airport commemorative
coin. 1972. (vg). Sold June 2010: £4

▲ BMW ashtray. (1980). (g).
Sold June 2010: £4.60

▲ Garfield telephone. 1986. (g).
Sold March 2010: £6

MISCELLANEOUS

▲ Melographic (piano) roll. (1910). (vg). Sold March 2010: £5

(Obverse)

(Reverse)

(Back)　　　(Side)

▲ Huntley & Palmers ginger nuts cardboard tube. 1912. (f). Sold March 2010: £12.10

▲ Cartwheel penny. 1797. (vg). Sold March 2010: £45.70

▲ Boots inhaler. (1930). (ex). Sold March 2010: £10.10

▲ Wooden rhino sculpture. (1965). (vg). Sold March 2010: £3.70

▲ Gatekeepers (David Winter cottage) model. 1988. (vg). Sold January 2010: £16

▲ Wooden clown bookends. (1975). (vg). Sold March 2010: £5.10

▲ Coca-Cola canvas bag. (1990). (ex). Sold January 2010: £4.70

▲ Golf Gentlemen playing cards. (1980). (vg). Sold January 2010: £6.60

▲ Timmy Willie ceramic plate. 2005. (ex-mnt). Sold July 2007: £6.10

MISCELLANEOUS

▲ Dinky Toys road sign set. 1953-1965. (vg). Sold July 2007: £70.10

▲ Swan pen box. (1925). (f). Sold March 2010: £1.30

▲ R White's soft drinks enamelled sign. (1965). 756 x 502mm. (f). Sold July 2007: £15

▲ Cheerio non-alcoholic champagne advertising board. (1937). 340 x 242mm. (vg). Sold July 2007: £10

▲ Taunton Autumn Gold Cider bar decoration. (1980). (vg). Sold January 2008: £9

▲ The Beatles cloth badge. (1990). (vg). Sold March 2010: £4.10

▲ Sunny Jim cloth doll. (1960). (g). Sold August 2007: £15.10

▲ Shell flag. (1960). 880 x 420mm. (vg). Sold August 2007: £25.60

▲ Pears' calendar. 1913. (g). Sold May 2010: £4

MISCELLANEOUS

▲ Sir Henry Doulton centenary mug. 1997. (vg). Sold July 2007: £4

▲ Corgi Model Club enamel pin badge. (1965). (vg-ex). Sold August 2007: £13.50

▲ Ghostbusters cartoon wall clock. 1986. (g). Sold January 2008: £3.50

▲ Lovable Louie porcelain clown. 1989. (ex). Sold January 2008: £10.10

▲ Utterly Butterly cooking timer. (2002). (ex). Sold January 2008: £12.20

▲ Royal Doulton Winnie the Pooh plate. (2000). (vg). Sold January 2008: £5

▲ Iron key. (1850). 145mm long. (vg). Sold August 2011: £4

▲ Wright brothers pewter sculpture. 1979. (vg-ex). Sold March 2011: £5

▲ Tinkers Club badge. (1955). (g-vg). Sold August 2011: £10.10

▲ Enid Blyton's Magazine Club pin badge. (1955). (vg). Sold September 2007: £15.20

▲ Mickey Mouse wristwatch. 1996. (vg). Sold September 2007: £10

MISCELLANEOUS

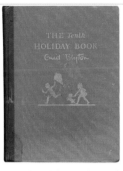

▲ Only Fools and Horses novelty teapot. (1990). (vg). Sold November 2007: £15

▲ The Tenth Holiday Book – Enid Blyton. 1955. (g). Sold June 2007: £4.20

▲ Royal Military Police wooden truncheon. (1965). (g). Sold October 2007: £30.10

▲ Christadelphian Youth Circle enamel badge. (1975). (vg). Sold June 2011: £3

▲ Royal Wedding horse brass. 1981. (vg). Sold January 2008: £3.10

▲ Homepride flour sifter. 1989. (g). Sold November 2007: £10

▲ Missouri Prison Board tin sign. (1970). (g). Sold September 2007: £25.10

▲ Gromit backpack. (2000). (ex). Sold November 2007: £9

▲ Butlin's plastic apron. (1980). (g). Sold October 2007: £6

MISCELLANEOUS

▲ The War Illustrated. Vol 9, No 217, 28 September 1945. (g). Sold August 2011: £4.10

▲ The Gillies Cottage (David Winter). 1988. (vg). Sold August 2011: £12.10

▲ Darth Maul (Star Wars) money box. (2000). (vg). Sold August 2011: £35.10

▲ British Bird stamp book (complete). 1971. (ex). Sold August 2011: £4

▲ Hit Boy 310 portable radio. (1980). (g). Sold November 2007: £12.10

▲ Safe Driving Award medal. (1955). (vg). Sold August 2011: £10.10

▲ Walkman keyring. (2000). (mnt). Sold August 2011: £5.20

▲ American bus ticket. September 1943. (f). Sold May 2011: £3.60

▲ The Ten Commandments movie publicity book. 1957. (vg). Sold August 2011: £40.10

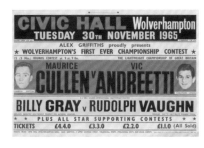

▲ Civic Hall boxing poster. 30 November 1965. (vg). Sold August 2011: £16.70

▲ Avon eagle bottle. (1975). (vg). Sold August 2011: £5

MISCELLANEOUS

▲ View-Master Model E Viewer. (1955). (g). Sold August 2011: £8

▲ AA patrolman's cloth badge. (1975). (vg). Sold August 2011: £4

▲ England's Glory branded envelope. 1902. (vg). Sold August 2011: £10.10

▲ Royal Wedding stamps. 1982. (mnt). Sold August 2011: £2.10

▲ 1939-45 Star medal. (vg-ex). Sold July 2011: £15.20

▲ Newbury enamel badge. 1988. (vg). Sold August 2011: £5.10

▲ Canadian Pacific luggage label. 1960. (vg-ex). Sold April 2011: £1.60

▲ Friary Meux enamel lapel badge. (1960). (vg). Sold August 2011: £8.10

▲ G Gale & Co Ltd glass bottle. (1910). (vg). Sold August 2011: £4.70

▲ New York lettercard. 1916. (g). Sold August 2011: £15.10

▲ Caravan Club grille badge. (1975). (vg). Sold August 2011: £7.20

▲ Beatles thimbles (set of 5). (1990). (vg). Sold August 2011: £10

MISCELLANEOUS

▲ Eagle comic. 19 November 1983. (g). Sold August 2011: £10

▲ Austria View-Master reels. 1967. (vg). Sold August 2011: £15.10

▲ Spring Story (Brambly Hedge) money box. 1989. (vg). Sold August 2011: £5.20

▲ Beatles bell jar. 1993. (f). Sold August 2011: £30.10

▲ Adventure for Boys diecast van. (1995). (ex). Sold July 2011: £10.10

▲ Errol Brown autograph on sheet music. 1976. (vg). Sold August 2011: £15.40

▲ Schools' Victory Message. June 1946. (g-vg). Sold July 2011: £40.60

▲ SMC Rover keyring. (1990). (vg). Sold July 2011: £5.20

▲ Wills's Star cigarettes packet. (1960). (vg). Sold July 2011: £15.10

▲ Union & Central brass belt buckle. (1985). (vg-ex). Sold July 2011: £10.10

▲ London & North Eastern Railway luggage label. 1947. (f). Sold July 2011: £2.10

▲ Fairy Soap tin advertising sign. (1950). (g). Sold June 2011: £50.10

▲ PG Tips playing cards. (1995). (vg). Sold July 2011: £5.20

▲ Donkey playing cards. (1950). (f). Sold July 2011: £3

▲ Old Salt Royal Doulton ceramic jug. 1960. (vg). Sold July 2011: £70.10

▲ Bugs Bunny Television Story Book. 1963. (f-g). Sold July 2011: £3.10

MISCELLANEOUS

▲ Bell's ashtray. (1975). (vg). Sold July 2011: £12.70

▲ Bill Pegg commemorative cover. 1983. (vg).Sold July 2011: £8.10

▲ BIA paper drinks coaster. (1965). (g). Sold July 2011: £1.30

▲ Funny Birds reel to reel tape. 1970. (g-vg). Sold June 2011: £2.30

▲ 2nd Model Brownie 127 camera. 1959-63. (vg). Sold June 2011: £3

▲ Hierarchy Centenary Congress badge. 1950. (vg). Sold June 2011: £2

▲ Films and Filming magazine. August 1976. (vg). Sold August 2011: £18.10

▲ HMV soft tone gramophone needles tin. (1960). (g-vg). Sold August 2011: £26.10

▲ The Royal Atlast Reader No 2 (book). 1897. (f). Sold August 2011: £4.10

▲ Tri-ang Hornby goods truck. (1970). (vg). Sold June 2011: £12.20

▲ Lotto board game. (1960). (vg). Sold June 2011: £3.10

▲ Conway Twitty CD. 2000. (vg).Sold August 2011: £3.10

▲ Totem Picture Library comic. No 5, 1961. (vg). Sold June 2011: £8.70

▲ Camel Lights phonecard. (1995). (ex-mnt). Sold June 2011: £8

▲ New York City guide. 12th printing of 1956 book. (vg). Sold June 2011: £9.20

▲ Picture Post magazine. 19 November 1955. (f). Sold June 2011: £5.10

▲ Kings Lynn v. Hackney Speedway programme. 1974. (vg). Sold June 2011: £2.10

▲ F.I.M Speedway Championship Final ticket. 8 September 1962. (g). Sold August 2011: £3.30

▲ England v Rest of the World ticket. 23 October 1963. (vg). Sold August 2011: £22.70

▲ Brass coronation souvenir money box. 1953. (vg). Sold August 2011: £10.20

▲ England's Glory Matches competition leaflet. 1902. (vg). Sold August 2011: £7.90

MISCELLANEOUS

▲ The Crazy Gang – Victoria Palace theatre programme. (1950). (g). Sold August 2011: £12.10

▲ London 1980 Stamp Exhibition miniature sheet. Sold August 2011: £1.20

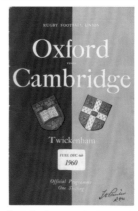

▲ Oxford v Cambridge rugby programme. 6 December 1960. (vg). Sold August 2011: £2.60

▲ Top Hat beer mat. (1960). (vg). Sold August 2011: £4.10

▲ RAC plastic grille badge. (1975). (vg). Sold August 2011: £3.10

▲ Mersey matchbox label. (1965). (ex). Sold August 2011: £1.30

▲ TT Races commemorative cover. 2005. (vg). Sold August 2011: £5.10

▲ 5000 Francs – Rwanda (banknote). 1998. (f). Sold August 2011: £3.60

▲ Letter from the Maharaja of Dhar's secretary. 1932. (g). Sold August 2011: £2.10

MISCELLANEOUS

▲ Record Mirror. 26 April 1980. (g). Sold August 2011: £2.60

▲ HMS Forester trade card. (1910). (vg). Sold August 2011: £2.30

▲ BOAC ceramic mug. (1965). (vg). Sold August 2011: £35.30

▲ View-Master reel album. (1960). (vg). Sold August 2011: £8

▲ Jersey Airport (BEA) postcard. (1960). (vg). Sold August 2011: £3.60

▲ Concorde matchbook. (1980). (vg). Sold August 2011: £6.10

▲ 10 Rupees – Sri Lanka (banknote). 1990. (g-vg). Sold August 2011: £3.10

▲ Heinz Invaders button badge. 1987. (ex). Sold October 2011: £1

▲ Spar button badge. (1975). (g). Sold October 2011: £2

▲ Royal Coronation Stage Coach diecast model. 1953. (vg). Sold October 2011: £40

MISCELLANEOUS

▲ Illustrated magazine. May 1958. (vg). Sold October 2011: £12.10

▲ RAC road map of Edinburgh. (1930). (vg). Sold October 2011: £4.10

▲ Reality periodical. 1916. (g). Sold October 2011: £3.60

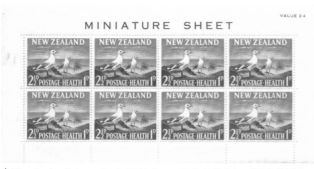

▲ New Zealand stamp sheet. 1964. (ex-mnt). Sold October 2011: £6.10

▲ Banks's Old Ale beer mat. (1980). (vg). Sold October 2011: £2.60

▲ Thor advertising leaflet. (1940). (g-vg). Sold October 2011: £3

▲ Sons And Lovers – DH Lawrence (paperback). 1948. (vg). Sold October 2011: £10.10

▲ Whitbread playing cards. (1985). (g-vg). Sold October 2011: £2.50

MISCELLANEOUS

▲ Butlin's spoon. (1965). (g-vg). Sold October 2011: £4.60

▲ Butlin's saving stamp. (1950). (ex). Sold October 2011: £10.10

▲ Ellesmere Female Society medal. 1811. (f). Sold October 2011: £6.10

▲ Arsenal FA Cup Final rosette. 1971. (g-vg). Sold October 2011: £15.10

▲ Postage economy label. (1943). (g-vg). Sold October 2011: £2.90

▲ England v Scotland football programme. 19 February 1944. (g). Sold October 2011: £65.30

▲ Peter Duncan publicity photograph. (1980). (vg). Sold October 2011: £4.20

▲ Bruce Forsyth autograph. Dedicated. Sold October 2011: £20.10

▲ Forth Railway Bridge BT phonecard. 1990. (vg). Sold October 2011: £7.10

▲ Patrick Tambay postcard. (1985). (vg). Sold October 2011: £2

▲ Ascot Authority Stand enamel badge. 1993. (vg). Sold October 2011: £4.10

MISCELLANEOUS

▲ Goodwood International Motor Racing programme. 11 April 1955. (f-g) Sold October 2011: £15.10

▲ The Lounge magazine. June 1929. (g). Sold October 2011: £4.70

▲ Nicolaus Silver shot glass. 1961. (vg). Sold October 2011: £8.20

▲ Wolverhampton crested china miniature cheese dish. (1990). (vg). Sold October 2011: £4

▲ Nottingham crested china miniature cheese dish. (1990). (vg). Sold October 2011: £4

▲ Halifax speedway enamel badge. 1958. (vg). Sold October 2011: £5.80

▲ Frame-Food Cocoa postcard. 1913. (vg). Sold October 2011: £19

▲ Playtime comic. 3 May 1919. (f-g). Sold October 2011: £6.10

▲ Teesside Park racecard. 1 June 1968. (vg). Sold October 2011: £3.60

▲ The Who: Maximum R&B (limpback book). 1996. (vg). Sold October 2011: £5.10

▲ Record Mirror & Disc periodical. 8 November 1975. (g). Sold October 2011: £7.40

▲ Rolling Stones concert ticket. 1990. (f). Sold October 2011: £2.60

▲ Oldsmobile Corgi diecast model. 1962-1966. (vg). Sold October 2011: £15

▲ Royal Tournament souvenir pro-gramme. 1956. (vg). Sold October 2011: £3.10

▲ Shand-Mason Fire Engine Matchbox diecast model. 1960. (vg). Sold October 2011: £25.10

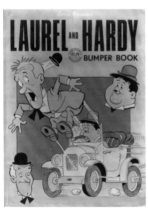

▲ Laurel and Hardy Bumper Book. 1970. (f). Sold October 2011: £2.30

▲ Crawford biscuit tin. (1915). (p-f). Sold October 2011: £3.60

MISCELLANEOUS

▲ Uncle Mac's Own Story Book. 1950. (f). Sold October 2011: £1.90

▲ Puck Annual. 1932. (p) Sold October 2011: £2.40

▲ The Western Film Annual. 1954. (g). Sold October 2011: £10.40

▲ Propert's Leather and Saddle Soap tin. (1950). (f). Sold October 2011: £1.20

▲ Golden Best beer pump sign. (1980). (vg). Sold October 2011: £3.10

▲ Mick McQuaid Cut Plug tin. (1935). (f). Sold October 2011: £3.20

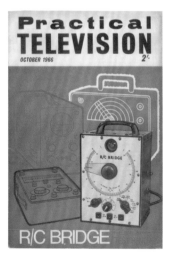

▲ Practical Television magazine. October 1966. (g). Sold October 2011: £1

▲ Skipping rope. (1965). (f). Sold October 2011: £1.50

▲ Fanta yo-yo. (1990). (f). Sold October 2011: £1

▲ Compound Glycerine & Thymol Pastille tin. (1950). (g). Sold October 2011: £1.20

▲ Super Draught half pint mug. (1975). (vg). Sold October 2011: £2

ROMAN NUMERALS

The Romans were active in trade and commerce so developed a non-positional decimal system that does not include a zero. The system persisted until the 14th century, when they were abandoned in favour of Arabic numerals; however, Roman numerals are still used in certain circumstances, such as to indicate the order of ruling monarchs. Anybody collecting old books or ephemera will find it useful to have a good knowledge of Roman numerals, because they are often used to represent published copyright dates.

Roman numerals make use of seven different symbols that are combined to form additions and subtractions that create all the numbers required. The symbols are:

I	=	1
V	=	5
X	=	10
L	=	50
C	=	100
D	=	500
M	=	1000

When forming numbers, the symbols are generally placed in order value, and then added together. For example:

MMD   =   2500.

However, sometimes smaller numbers are placed in front of larger numbers, and in these situations the smaller values are subtracted from the larger value immediately following. For example:

XL	=	40	(50 – 10)
XLIV	=	44	((50 – 10) + (5-1))
CXLIX	=	149	(100 + (50-10) + (10 -1))

Very large numbers are indicated by putting horizontal lines over them, which means the value is multiplied by 1000. So, a V with a line over the top indicates 5000.

1	I
2	II
3	III
4	IV
5	V
6	VI
7	VII
8	VIII
9	IX
10	X
11	XI
12	XII
15	XV
20	XX
30	XXX
40	XL
50	L
60	LX
70	LXX
80	LXXX
90	XC
100	C
200	CC
300	CCC
400	CD
500	D
600	DC
700	DCC
800	DCCC
900	CM
1000	M
1500	MD
2000	MM

EPHEMERA REFERENCE NUMBERS

There are many ways of dating an item of paper ephemera, from the material it is made out of, the way the date is formatted, the way it is printed, or even down to the type of ink scribbled on it.

Many items of ephemera can be identified from a reference number allocated on the printed matter.

Example one:

A Home Office booklet could have a reference 407659 7/27

In this case, the last three digits give the clue to the publishing date:

July 1927.

Example two:

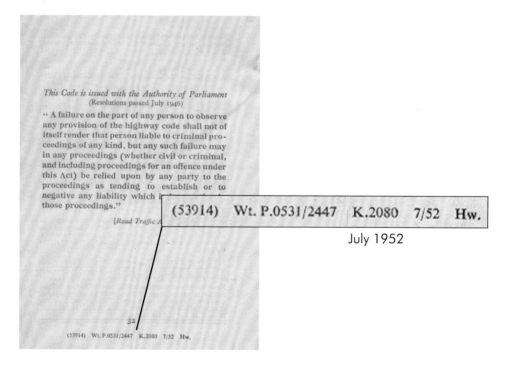

This Code is issued with the Authority of Parliament
(Resolutions passed July 1946)

" A failure on the part of any person to observe any provision of the highway code shall not of itself render that person liable to criminal pro- ceedings of any kind, but any such failure may in any proceedings (whether civil or criminal, and including proceedings for an offence under this Act) be relied upon by any party to the proceedings as tending to establish or to negative any liability which i those proceedings."

[*Road Traffic A*

(53914)   Wt. P.0531/2447   K.2080   7/52   Hw.

July 1952

EPHEMERA DATE IDENTIFIER

When a day of the week and the month is known and a specific year is only suspected, the charts on the following pages will help confirm the year. However, it must be stressed that this is merely a guide.

Instructions:

1. Use List 1 to link a letter (between A and N) to your chosen year.

2. Refer to List 2 and select the relevant letter from those running across the top.

3. Go to the known month and read off the number between 01 and 28.

4. Refer to List 3 and select the relevant number between 01 and 28, this will then give you the day of the week.

Example:
If you have a day and month (Monday 12th August) and suspect that the year is 1963, select column D in List 2, then go to box 14 in List 3. This confirms your suspicion because the 12th August 1963 was a Monday.

LIST 1

					1800-E	1801-A
1802-B	1803-C	1804-H	1805-D	1806-E	1807-A	1808-I
1809-F	1810-G	1811-D	1812-J	1813-B	1814-C	1815-F
1816-K	1817-E	1818-A	1819-B	1820-L	1821-G	1822-D
1823-E	1824-M	1825-C	1826-F	1827-G	1828-N	1829-A
1830-B	1831-C	1832-H	1833-D	1834-E	1835-A	1836-I
1837-F	1838-G	1839-D	1840-J	1841-B	1842-C	1843-F
1844-K	1845-E	1846-A	1847-B	1848-L	1849-G	1850-D
1851-E	1852-M	1853-C	1854-F	1855-G	1856-N	1857-A
1858-B	1859-C	1860-H	1861-D	1862-E	1863-A	1864-I
1865-F	1866-G	1867-D	1868-J	1869-B	1870-C	1871-F
1872-K	1873-E	1874-A	1875-B	1876-L	1877-G	1878-D
1879-E	1880-M	1881-C	1882-F	1883-G	1884-N	1885-A
1886-B	1887-C	1888-H	1889-D	1890-E	1891-A	1892-I
1893-F	1894-G	1895-D	1896-J	1897-B	1898-C	1899-F
1900-G	1901-D	1902-E	1903-A	1904-I	1905-F	1906-G
1907-D	1908-J	1909-B	1910-C	1911-F	1912-K	1913-E
1914-A	1915-B	1916-L	1917-G	1918-D	1919-E	1920-M
1921-C	1922-F	1923-G	1924-N	1925-A	1926-B	1927-C
1928-H	1929-D	1930-E	1931-A	1932-I	1933-F	1934-G
1935-D	1936-J	1937-B	1938-C	1939-F	1940-K	1941-E
1942-A	1943-B	1944-L	1945-G	1946-D	1947-E	1948-M
1949-C	1950-F	1951-G	1952-N	1953-A	1954-B	1955-C
1956-H	1957-D	1958-E	1959-A	1960-I	1961-F	1962-G
1963-D	1964-J	1965-B	1966-C	1967-F	1968-K	1969-E
1970-A	1971-B	1972-L	1973-G	1974-D	1975-E	1976-M
1977-C	1978-F	1979-G	1980-N	1981-A	1982-B	1983-C
1984-H	1985-D	1986-E	1987-A	1988-I	1989-F	1990-G
1991-D	1992-J	1993-B	1994-C	1995-F	1996-K	1997-E
1998-A	1999-B	2000-L	2001-G	2002-D	2003-E	2004-M
2005-C	2006-F					

LIST 2

	A	B	C	D	E	F	G	H	I	J	K	L	M	N
Jan.	14	20	19	16	15	18	17	18	20	15	17	19	14	16
Feb.	11	10	09	06	05	08	07	01	03	12	28	02	04	27
Mar.	18	17	16	20	19	15	14	14	16	18	20	15	17	19
Apr.	22	21	13	24	23	26	25	25	13	22	24	26	21	23
May	20	19	18	15	14	17	16	16	18	20	15	17	19	14
June	24	23	22	26	25	21	13	13	22	24	26	21	23	25
July	15	14	20	17	16	19	18	18	20	15	17	19	14	16
Aug.	19	18	17	14	20	16	15	15	17	19	14	16	18	20
Sep.	23	22	21	25	24	13	26	26	21	23	25	13	22	24
Oct.	14	20	19	16	15	18	17	17	19	14	16	18	20	15
Nov.	25	24	23	13	26	22	21	21	23	25	13	22	24	26
Dec.	16	15	14	18	17	20	19	19	14	16	18	20	15	17

LIST 3

1

Su	Mo	Tu	We	Th	Fr	Sa
			01	02	03	04
05	06	07	08	09	10	11
12	13	14	15	16	17	18
19	20	21	22	23	24	25
26	27	28	29			

2

Su	Mo	Tu	We	Th	Fr	Sa
		01	02	03	04	05
06	07	08	09	10	11	12
13	14	15	16	17	18	19
20	21	22	23	24	25	26
27	28	29				

3

Su	Mo	Tu	We	Th	Fr	Sa
	01	02	03	04	05	06
07	08	09	10	11	12	13
14	15	16	17	18	19	20
21	22	23	24	25	26	27
28	29					

4

Su	Mo	Tu	We	Th	Fr	Sa
01	02	03	04	05	06	07
08	09	10	11	12	13	14
15	16	17	18	19	20	21
22	23	24	25	26	27	28
29						

5

Su	Mo	Tu	We	Th	Fr	Sa
						01
02	03	04	05	06	07	08
09	10	11	12	13	14	15
16	17	18	19	20	21	22
23	24	25	26	27	28	

6

Su	Mo	Tu	We	Th	Fr	Sa
					01	02
03	04	05	06	07	08	09
10	11	12	13	14	15	16
17	18	19	20	21	22	23
24	25	26	27	28		

7

Su	Mo	Tu	We	Th	Fr	Sa
				01	02	03
04	05	06	07	08	09	10
11	12	13	14	15	16	17
18	19	20	21	22	23	24
25	26	27	28			

8

Su	Mo	Tu	We	Th	Fr	Sa
		01	02	03	04	
05	06	07	08	09	10	11
12	13	14	15	16	17	18
19	20	21	22	23	24	25
26	27	28				

9

Su	Mo	Tu	We	Th	Fr	Sa
		01	02	03	04	05
06	07	08	09	10	11	12
13	14	15	16	17	18	19
20	21	22	23	24	25	26
27	28					

10

Su	Mo	Tu	We	Th	Fr	Sa
	01	02	03	04	05	06
07	08	09	10	11	12	13
14	15	16	17	18	19	20
21	22	23	24	25	26	27
28						

11

Su	Mo	Tu	We	Th	Fr	Sa
01	02	03	04	05	06	07
08	09	10	11	12	13	14
15	16	17	18	19	20	21
22	23	24	25	26	27	28

12

Su	Mo	Tu	We	Th	Fr	Sa
						01
02	03	04	05	06	07	08
09	10	11	12	13	14	15
16	17	18	19	20	21	22
23	24	25	26	27	28	29

13

Su	Mo	Tu	We	Th	Fr	Sa
					01	02
03	04	05	06	07	08	09
10	11	12	13	14	15	16
17	18	19	20	21	22	23
24	25	26	27	28	29	30

14

Su	Mo	Tu	We	Th	Fr	Sa
				01	02	03
04	05	06	07	08	09	10
11	12	13	14	15	16	17
18	19	20	21	22	23	24
25	26	27	28	29	30	31

15

Su	Mo	Tu	We	Th	Fr	Sa
			01	02	03	04
05	06	07	08	09	10	11
12	13	14	15	16	17	18
19	20	21	22	23	24	25
26	27	28	29	30	31	

16

Su	Mo	Tu	We	Th	Fr	Sa
		01	02	03	04	05
06	07	08	09	10	11	12
13	14	15	16	17	18	19
20	21	22	23	24	25	26
27	28	29	30	31		

LIST 3 CONTINUED...

17

Su	Mo	Tu	We	Th	Fr	Sa
	01	02	03	04	05	06
07	08	09	10	11	12	13
14	15	16	17	18	19	20
21	22	23	24	25	26	27
28	29	30	31			

18

Su	Mo	Tu	We	Th	Fr	Sa
01	02	03	04	05	06	07
08	09	10	11	12	13	14
15	16	17	18	19	20	21
22	23	24	25	26	27	28
29	30	31				

19

Su	Mo	Tu	We	Th	Fr	Sa
						01
02	03	04	05	06	07	08
09	10	11	12	13	14	15
16	17	18	19	20	21	22
23	24	25	26	27	28	29
30	31					

20

Su	Mo	Tu	We	Th	Fr	Sa
					01	02
03	04	05	06	07	08	09
10	11	12	13	14	15	16
17	18	19	20	21	22	23
24	25	26	27	28	29	30
31						

21

Su	Mo	Tu	We	Th	Fr	Sa
				01	02	03
04	05	06	07	08	09	10
11	12	13	14	15	16	17
18	19	20	21	22	23	24
25	26	27	28	29	30	

22

Su	Mo	Tu	We	Th	Fr	Sa
				01	02	03	04
05	06	07	08	09	10	11
12	13	14	15	16	17	18
19	20	21	22	23	24	25
26	27	28	29	30		

LIST 3 CONTINUED...

23

Su	Mo	Tu	We	Th	Fr	Sa
		01	02	03	04	05
06	07	08	09	10	11	12
13	14	15	16	17	18	19
20	21	22	23	24	25	26
27	28	29	30			

24

Su	Mo	Tu	We	Th	Fr	Sa
	01	02	03	04	05	06
07	08	09	10	11	12	13
14	15	16	17	18	19	20
21	22	23	24	25	26	27
28	29	30				

25

Su	Mo	Tu	We	Th	Fr	Sa
01	02	03	04	05	06	07
08	09	10	11	12	13	14
15	16	17	18	19	20	21
22	23	24	25	26	27	28
29	30					

26

Su	Mo	Tu	We	Th	Fr	Sa
						01
02	03	04	05	06	07	08
09	10	11	12	13	14	15
16	17	18	19	20	21	22
23	24	25	26	27	28	29
30						

27

Su	Mo	Tu	We	Th	Fr	Sa
					01	02
03	04	05	06	07	08	09
10	11	12	13	14	15	16
17	18	19	20	21	22	23
24	25	26	27	28	29	

28

Su	Mo	Tu	We	Th	Fr	Sa
				01	02	03
04	05	06	07	08	09	10
11	12	13	14	15	16	17
18	19	20	21	22	23	24
25	26	27	28	29		

OLD MONEY

d	= pence. One penny = 1d.
s	= shilling (bob). One shilling = 1/-.
£ (or L)	= pound (quid). 20/- = £1.
6d	= Sixpence (tanner).
12d	= Twelve pence (1/-).

Half Crown	= 2/6d.
Florin	= 2/-.
Crown	= 5/-.

Decimal equivalent

240d	= £1 (100 new pence).
Ten shillings	= 50p.
2/-	= 10p.
1/-	= 5p.

	OLD VALUE	CEASED CIRCULATION
Farthing	¼ d	1956
Half penny	½ d	1967
One penny	1d	1967
Three pence (silver)	3d	1944
Three pence (bronze)	3d	1967
Groat	4d	1887
Six pence	6d	1967
One shilling	1/-	1967
Two shillings (Florin)	2/-	1967
Half Crown	2/6d	1967
Crown	5/-	Still minted today with £5 face value.
Ten shilling note	10/-	Last printed 1969
One pound note	£1	1983

HALLMARK IDENTIFICATION

British hallmarks (a guarantee of an item's purity or quality) include a purity mark, an assay office mark, a date (letter), and sometimes a maker's mark.

On gold:
The purity mark of a crown with the carat was used from 1798 to 1975, but in Scotland a thistle replaced the crown.

From 1798 to 1854 only gold assays at 18ct and 22ct were hallmarked, with 9ct, 12ct, and 15ct being introduced thereafter. The fineness (in thousandths) was added for the period 1854 to 1932.

After 1975, gold marks were standardised and the only marks used were the crown and the fineness in thousandths, along with the place of assay and the date (letter).

On silver:
The lion passant means sterling silver, but as with gold, a thistle was used on Scottish products until 1975. Some items made of a higher Britannia silver standard were marked with the figure of Britannia instead of the lion. All items produced between 1697 and 1720 carry the Britannia mark.

The origin of an item can be determined by its assay mark:

 London's leopard head. First used 1300.
The leopard was crowned during the period 1478 - 1822.

 Birmingham's anchor. First used 1773.
Usually marked sideways on gold and upright on silver.

 Chester's shield. First used 1701. Last used 1962.

 Dublin's harp. First used 1636.

 Edinburgh's castle. First used 1681. Last used 1974.

 Exeter's castle. First used 1701. Last used 1883.

 Glasgow's tree insignia. First used 1681. Last used 1964.

 Newcastle's three towers. First used 1702. Last used 1884.

 Sheffield's crown. First used 1773.

 York's pennant flag. First used 1560. Last used 1858.

Special note: Watch out for the special 'year 2000' cross hallmark introduced for some items to celebrate the Millennium.

HALLMARK IDENTIFICATION (DATE LETTERS)

Each assay office has its own cycle of hallmarks, which include a letter for each year.

Year letter cycles start at A and usually end at Z. However, some cycles end before the letter Z is reached, and some cycles do not include the letter J.

In order to distinguish between years, in each cycle the letters are designed differently. For example, with a London hallmark the letter M signifying a date of 1807 is significantly different to the M used in the next cycle (which signifies a date of 1827).

There are hundreds of different date letters, too many to list in a book of this size, but thankfully there are plenty of good hallmark and date letter guides available in books and on the Internet.

BRITISH PATENT NUMBERS

There was never a set rule on how to cite a British patent on an item.

Older items often have only the name of the inventor or the company. Some items have application numbers even if the patent wasn't granted.

British patents were not issued with numbers until October 1852. Numbers were then issued retrospectively to 1617, as well as forward from then on. It is not likely that an item made before 1852 will have a patent number.

The following tables should help you to identify the year of many British patent numbers.

BRITISH PATENTS (1617 - 1852)

Until 1852 patents were acquired through a system that required visiting seven different offices and two signatures by the monarch.

Patents granted under this system were not numbered, but following the modernisation of the patent law in 1852, 14359 patents up to that date were given numbers retrospectively.

The following chart gives the earliest patent number issued for each of the years in the period.

All numbers in the table would be appended by a slash and the year of issue. For example, the earliest patent number issued for 1617 would be displayed as: 'no. 2/1617'.

YEAR	EARLIEST PATENT NO	YEAR	EARLIEST PATENT NO
1617	2	1780	1243
1630	49	1790	1720
1640	124	1800	2367
1660	128	1805	2807
1670	159	1810	3291
1680	210	1815	3871
1690	263	1820	4428
1700	365	1825	5064
1710	396	1830	5879
1720	425	1835	6743
1730	514	1840	8331
1740	570	1845	10453
1750	652	1850	12918
1760	744	1852	14359
1770	949		

BRITISH PATENTS (1852 - 1915)

In this period, patent applications filed were numbered starting at 1 each year. Any patents granted would retain the same number.

This means that patent numbers were regularly repeated during this period.

The following chart gives the number of patent applications in each year. This number also indicates the highest possible patent number granted for each of those years.

YEAR	NUMBER OF APPLICATIONS	YEAR	NUMBER OF APPLICATIONS
1852 - 53	4256	1885	16101
1854	2764	1886	17174
1855	2958	1887	18051
1856	3106	1888	19103
1857	3200	1889	21008
1858	3007	1890	21307
1859	3000	1891	22878
1860	3196	1892	24179
1861	3276	1893	25107
1862	3490	1894	25386
1863	3309	1895	25062
1864	3260	1896	30193
1865	3386	1897	30958
1866	3453	1898	27650
1867	3723	1899	25800
1868	3991	1900	23924
1869	3786	1901	26788
1870	3405	1902	28972
1871	3529	1903	28854
1872	3970	1904	29702
1873	4294	1905	27577
1874	4492	1906	30030
1875	4561	1907	28915
1876	5069	1908	28598
1877	4949	1909	30603
1878	5343	1910	30388
1879	5338	1911	29353
1880	5517	1912	30089
1881	5751	1913	30077
1882	6241	1914	24820
1883	5993	1915	18191
1884	17110		

BRITISH PATENTS (1916 - 1981)

Since 1916 published patents have been numbered in a series starting at 100,001.

After 1916 it is generally the case that only granted patents were published, and there is no information available for those that were not granted.

Numbers are preceded by the letters 'GB' to denote a Great British patent number.

The following table shows the earliest patent number published for each year from 1916 up to and including 1981.

YEAR	EARLIEST PATENT NO	YEAR	EARLIEST PATENT NO
1916	100,001	1949	614,704
1917	102,812	1950	633,754
1918	112,131	1951	650,021
1919	121,611	1952	667,061
1920	136,852	1953	687,841
1921	155,801	1954	704,741
1922	173,241	1955	724,991
1923	190,732	1956	745,421
1924	208,751	1957	768,941
1925	226,571	1958	791,071
1926	244,801	1959	809,321
1927	263,501	1960	829,181
1928	282,701	1961	861,801
1929	302,941	1962	889,571
1930	323,171	1963	918,311
1931	340,201	1964	949,031
1932	363,615	1965	982,551
1933	385,258	1966	1,015,491
1934	407,311	1967	1,058,501
1935	421,246	1968	1,102,801
1936	439,856	1969	1,142,501
1937	458,491	1970	1,180,651
1938	477,016	1971	1,222,451
1939	497,409	1972	1,263,601
1940	512,178	1973	1,306,401
1941	530,617	1974	1,346,401
1942	542,024	1975	1,384,031
1943	550,067	1976	1,424,101
1944	558,091	1977	1,464,401
1945	566,191	1978	1,500,801
1946	574,006	1979	1,540,351
1947	583,360	1980	1,560,781
1948	595,746	1981	1,584,611

BRITISH PATENTS (1979 - PRESENT)

The Patent Act of 1977 started January 1, 1978. Patent applications filed under the act are published 18 months after their priority date (so the first patents under the act were published 1979).

The numbers under the Patent Act start at 2,000,001. Patents filed before the introduction of the Patent Act, but published after, still used the old numbering system (see previous table).

The letters 'GB' before the number denote that it is a Great British patent number.

YEAR	EARLIEST PATENT NO
1979	2,000,001
1980	2,023,381
1981	2,050,131
1982	2,078,071
1983	2,100,561
1984	2,121,661
1985	2,141,611
1986	2,160,751
1987	2,176,681
1988	2,192,121
1989	2,206,271
1990	2,220,118
1991	2,232,862
1992	2,245,131
1993	2,257,003
1994	2,268,036
1995	2,279,218
1996	2,290,445
1997	2,302,005
1998	2,314,495
1999	2,326,809
2000	2,338,877
2001	2,351,428
2002	2,363,560
2003	2,377,151
2004	2,390,285
2005	2,403,389
2006	2,415,592
2007	2,427,532
2008	2,439,518

THE REIGN OF BRITISH MONARCHS FROM 1714

GEORGE I	1714 - 1727
GEORGE II	1727 - 1760
GEORGE III	1760 - 1820
GEORGE IV	1820 - 1830
WILLIAM IV	1830 - 1837
VICTORIA	1837 - 1901
EDWARD VII	1901 - 1910
GEORGE V	1910 - 1936
EDWARD VIII	1936 - 1936
GEORGE VI	1936 - 1952
ELIZABETH II	1952 - present

Special note:

Items bearing the Tudor Crown (arched top) will date from 1902 to 1952.

Anything made after 1952 will bear the St Edwards Crown (which has an arch on either side of the top cross).

ACRONYMS

AA	American Airlines.
AA	Automobile Association.
ACF	Automobile Club de France.
AD	Anno Domini.
AFS	Auxiliary Fire Service.
AMC	Army Medical Corps.
ARP	Air Raid Precautions.
ASA	Advertising Standards Authority.
ASC	Army Service Corps.
AT&T	American Telephone and Telegraph.
BA	British Airways (formerly BEA).
BBC	British Broadcasting Corporation.
BBFC	British Board of Film Classification.
BC	Before Christ.
BC	British Columbia.
BEA	British European Airways.
BEF	British Expeditionary Forces.
BM	British Midland (airline).
BMA	British Medical Association.
BMC	British Motor Corporation.
BMW	Bayerische Motoren Werke.
BO	British Officer.
BOAC	British Overseas Airway Corporation.
BP	Blue Peter.
BP	British Petroleum.
BR	British Rail.
BSA	Birmingham Small Arms.
BSI	British Standards Institution.
BT	British Telecommunications.
DC	Detective Comics.
DJ	Dust Jacket (of a book).
DVD	Digital Versatile Disc.

EP	Extended Play (record).
EU	European Union.
GMC	General Medical Council.
GMC	General Motors Corporation.
HA	Health Authority.
HM	Her (or His) Majesty.
HMS	Her (or His) Majesty's Ship.
HRH	Her (or His) Royal Highness.
ISBN	International Standard Book Number.
ISO	International Standards Organisation.
ITV	International Television.
KLM	Royal Dutch Airline.
LP	Long Playing (record).
MBE	Member of the Order of the British Empire.
MC	Military Cross.
MGM	Metro Goldwyn Mayer.
MP	Member of Parliament
MP	Military Police.
MS	Manuscript.
MS	Microsoft.
MS	Motor Ship.
NATO	North Atlantic Treaty Organisation.
NCO	Non-Commissioned Officer.
NHS	National Health Service.
NSC	National Screening Committee.
NTWF	National Transport Workers' Federation.
OBE	Officer of the Order of the British Empire.
PO	Petty Officer.
PO	Post Office.
P&O	Pacific and Orient.
RA	Royal Academy.
RA	Royal Artillery.
RAC	Royal Armoured Corps.
RAC	Royal Automobile Club.

RAF	Royal Air Force.
RAOC	Royal Army Ordnance Corps.
RASC	Royal Army Service Corps (ASC prior to 1918).
RCT	Royal Corps of Transport.
RE	Royal Engineers.
REME	Royal Electrical and Mechanical Engineers.
RM	Royal Mail.
RMS	Royal Mail Ship.
RMS	Royal Merchant Ship.
RoSPA	Royal Society for the Prevention of Accidents.
RPM	Revolutions Per Minute.
RR	Rolls-Royce.
RSPB	Royal Society for the Protection of Birds.
RSPCA	Royal Society for the Prevention of Cruelty to Animals.
RSPCC	Royal Society for the Prevention of Cruelty to Children.
SNCF	Societe Nationale des Chemins de fer Francais.
SS	Steam Ship.
TA	Territorial Army.
TGWU	Transport and General Workers Union.
TRH	Their Royal Highnesses.
TWA	Trans World Airlines.
UN	United Nations.
USAF	United States Air Force.
USS	United States Ship.
VAT	Value Added Tax.
VHS	Video Home System.
WCW	World Championship Wrestling.
WO	Warrant Officer.
WWE	World Wrestling Entertainment.
WWF	World Wildlife Fund.
WWW	World Wide Web.

SUBJECT TERMINOLOGY AND GLOSSARY

ACETATE - A record pressing made of aluminium with a coating of vinyl-like material, used for checking the quality of work in progress being recorded by a producer and artist. They are only designed for a few plays as the coating quickly wears out.

ADDORSED - Back to back.

AERONAUTICA - Collectable items relating to aircraft.

AEROPHILATELY - The collecting of air mail stamps and covers.

ALLOY - A mixture of metals.

AMERICANA - Items that are distinctive of America.

ANTHOLOGY - Collection of literary passages and works.

ARABESQUE - Symmetrical decoration in the form of flowing lines of branches, leaves and scrolling.

ARCTOPHILY - The collecting of teddy bears.

ARGYROTHECOLOGY - The collection and study of money boxes.

ART DÉCO - A style of interior decoration and manufactured objects, of the period (approximately) 1925 – 1940. Symmetrical designs adapted to mass production.

ART NOUVEAU - A style of decoration of the early 20th century. Based on soft curves and influenced by the example of Japanese art (particularly leaves and flowers).

ARTEFACT - An object shaped by human craft (such as a tool), usually with archaeological significance.

ASTROPHILATELY - Space related postage stamps.

AUDIOPHILY - The collecting of recorded sound.

AURICULAR - Shaped like the ear.

AUTOMOBILIA - Items relating to motor vehicles.

BACK STAMP - A maker's marking on the underside of a ceramic piece. (Back Stamps scored through, indicate 'seconds').

BANDOPHILY - The collecting of cigar bands.

BEZEL - The metal frame around the glass of a watch or clock.

BIBLIOLOGY - The study of books.

BIBLIOPHILY - The collecting of books.

BIBLIOTICS - The study of documents to determine their authenticity.

BOOTERS - Buyers at a car boot sale.

BOXWOOD - Close grained light yellow wood of the box. A mustard spoon could typically be made of boxwood.

BREWERIANA - Collectable items related to brewing.

BUFFED - Condition description for a vinyl record, where the surface looks as though it has been buffed with wire wool. In other words, the surface is multi scratched in poor condition.

CAGOPHILY - The collecting of keys.

CAMEO - A shell or stone carved in relief, in such a way that brings out the different colours of the material used.

CARD CASE - A case (usually with an ornate design) to carry calling/business cards. Originated in 18th century France.

CARTOGRAPHY - The study, making, and collecting of maps.

CARTOPHILY - The collecting of cigarette cards.

CAST IRON - Ironwork produced by pouring molten iron into a pre-shaped mould.

CERAMICS - The generic term for pottery, porcelain, terracotta, etc.

CHINOISERIE - Decorative artwork with Chinese characteristics.

CHIROGRAPHY - The study of handwriting.

CHRYSOLOGY - The study of precious metals.

CHURCHILLANIA - Collectable items relating to Winston Churchill.

CLYVESOPHILY - Collecting of mugs.

CODICOLOGY - The study of early manuscripts.

CONCHOLOGY - The study of shells.

COPOCLEPHILY - The collecting of key rings.

COTTAPENSOPHILY - Collecting of coat hangers.

CRAZING - A fine network of cracks in the glaze of pottery and porcelain.

CRIMINOLOGY - The study of criminals and crime.

CRYPTOLOGY - The study of codes.

DACTYLIOLOGY - The study of rings.

DECAL - Short for decalcomania. The art or process of transferring a design from prepared paper onto another surface.

DELFTWARE - Earthenware named after the Dutch town of Delft.

DELTIOLOGY - The collecting of postcards.

DIECAST - Zinc alloy used to manufacture toys, enabling the production of strong, shiny, bright, permanently decorated items.

DIGITABULIST - The collecting of thimbles.

DISCOPHILY - The collecting of recorded music.

DISNEYANA - Collectable items relating to Disney.

EARTHENWARE - Glazed pottery fired to a temperature of approximately 1000 degrees C. Normally red or brown with a low chipping resistance.

ECCLESIOLOGY - The study and collection of items relating to church.

EDWARDIAN - Relating to the period of the reign of King Edward VII (1901 – 1910).

EGYPTOLOGY - The study of Ancient Egypt.

ENAMEL - A semi-opaque form of glass fused on to metal surfaces to decorate them.

ENCRUST - To ornament by overlaying with a crust of something precious.

ENIGMATOLOGY - The study and collecting of puzzles.

EPHEMERA - Anything designed to be used and then thrown away, usually made of paper. For example, old bus tickets and cigarette packets.

EPNS - Electro Plated Silver Nickel - silver plate.

EROTICA - Glamour related items.

ESCAPEMENT - Mechanical device that regulates the movement in a watch or clock.

ESCUTCHEON - Protective plate around a key hole, etc. Also in nautical terms – a ship's nameplate affixed to the stern.

ETYMOLOGY - The study of the origin of words.

EXONUMIA - The US word for coin-like objects (and the collecting of them).

FLATWARE- Tableware that is relatively flat and fashioned as a single unit (e.g. the meal-tray supplied by airlines). Also flat cutlery.

FLIPBACK - Vinyl record (picture) sleeve, laminated on the front only, with short fold-overs on the reverse. Most common in the sixties.

FOXING - Discolouration of paper, wood, etc., with spots through ageing and mildew.

FRESCO - The art of painting in water-colour on plaster or mortar when not quite dry.

FROMOLOGY - Cheese label collecting.

FUSILATELY - The collecting of phone cards.

GEMMOLOGY - The study of jewels and gems.

GEORGIAN - Relating to the period of the four King Georges, 1714 – 1830.

GILDED - Covered with a thin layer of gold.

GLYPTOGRAPHY - The art of engraving on gemstones.

GLYPTOLOGY - The study of gem engravings.

GNOMONICS - Items relating to the measuring of time with sundials.

GUTTER - The selvedge (borders) of a sheet of postage stamps, either unprinted or with plate numbers or other markings.

HALLMARK - A mark punched on to articles to guarantee a statutory degree of purity. Four stamps are; maker's mark, mark of quality, mark of the hall of Assay, and the year mark.

HISTORIOGRAPHY - The study of writing history.

HISTORIOLOGY - Study of history.

HOPLOLOGY - The study of weaponry.

HOROGRAPHY - The art of constructing sundials or clocks.

HOROLOGY - The science of time measurement.

HOSTELAPHILY - The collecting of outdoor signs from inns.

HYMNOGRAPHY - The study of writing hymns.

HYMNOLOGY - The study of hymns.

ICONOLOGY - The study of icons and symbols.

INFUNABULIST - See 'Bandophily'.

JUVENALIA - Children's play items.

KITCHENALIA - Items relating to a kitchen.

KITSCH - Arguably, a tacky version of 'retro'. Popular because of its garishness and links to a particular era (largely 50s/60s/70s).

LABEORPHILY - The collecting of beer bottle labels.

LACLABPHILY - See 'Fromology'.

LACQUER - The application of several layers of paint and special varnish to produce a decorative surface.

LAPIDARY - Cutting and engraving precious stones.

LEPIDOPTEROLOGY - The study of butterflies and moths.

LITHOGRAPHY - A process of printing dating back to the end of the eighteenth century (discovered in Germany). The principle being that oil and water do not mix. The image is drawn with a special applicator on a flat surface over which water is then passed. When covered with ink, only the applied area will accept it.

LOTOLOGY - The collecting of scratch cards and lottery related items.

LUCITE - Transparent thermoplastic acrylic resin.

LUSTRE - A glaze - surface coating for ceramics creating shine.

MAGIRICS - The art of cookery.

MATT GLAZE - A dull-surfaced glaze, non-reflecting.

MEMORABILIA - Items to commemorate memorable events.

MILITARIA - Collecting of materials or objects relating to the military.

MISCELLANY - A whole variety of objects. Miscellaneous items.

MODERNIST - A style characteristic of modern times.

MYTHOLOGY - The study of myths and fables.

NETSUKE - Traditional Japanese clothing, such as the kimono, had no pockets, so it was necessary for people to carry items like pipes and tobacco in containers called sagemono. These sagemono were hung from the sash of the kimono (the obi), and were secured in place using specially carved toggles known as net-suke.

NOTAPHILY - The collecting of bank notes.

NUMISMATICS - The collecting of and study of coins.

OBJECTS OF VIRTU - Fine art objects and antiques.

OBJETS D'ART - As 'objects of virtu'.

OBVERSE - The side of a coin, or medal, on which the head or principal design is shown. The other side of the coin is called the 'reverse'.

OENOLOGY - The study of wine.

OLEOGRAPH - A lithographic reproduction of an oil painting.

OOLOGY - The collecting of and study of bird's eggs.

OPERCULISM - Collecting of milk tops.

PALAEOBIOLOGY - The study of fossil plants and animals.

PALEONTOLOGY - The study of ancient life and fossils.

PAPIER-MACHE - Layers of paper shredded into a pulp and then pressed into shapes.

PAPYROLOGY - The study of paper.

PARANUMISTMATICA - The UK word for coin-like objects (and the collecting of them). A sub-category of 'Numismatics'.

PARAPHERNALIA - Miscellany associated with particular interests and items.

PARURE - A full matching jewellery set comprising necklace, brooch, bracelet, and earrings.

PETROLIANA - Gas and oil related items.

PHILATELY - Stamp collecting and the study of postal history.

PHILLUMENY - The collecting of matchboxes and matchbox labels.

PHILOGRAPHY - Autograph collecting.

PHILOMETRY - Collecting of First Day Covers.

PHONOPHILY - See 'Discophily'.

PICTURE DISC - A record pressed on clear vinyl, the middle of which is sandwiched with a picture. These are sometimes in shapes other than circular.

PORCELAIN - White form of stoneware usually translucent. Hard and non-porous. The most highly refined of all clay bodies and requiring the highest firing.

PRODUCTION STILLS - Are photographs taken during the production of a motion picture. They are usually shot during principal photography, and show the interaction between the actors and director, camera crew, makeup and wardrobe department, or stunt team.

PROOF - Early impression of a stamp, coin or medal, struck as a specimen.

PROVENANCE - Proof of past ownership or of authenticity.

RAILWAYANA - Collectable items relating to the railway.

REGENCY - The style of furniture, buildings, literature etc., popular in Great Britain 1811 – 1820.

RETRO - A fashion design, décor or style reminiscent of things past.

RETRO CHIC - Stylish and elegant retro.

RETROPHILIA - A love for things of the past.

REVERSE - Of a coin or medal (see 'Obverse').

RHYKENOLOGY - The collection and study of woodworking tools.

ROCOCO - Typically European architectural and decorative asymmetrical designs of the first half of the eighteenth century.

RPM - (Revolutions per minute), the speed at which a record is designed to play.

SCRIPOPHILY - The collecting of old financial documents, such as stocks and bonds certificates.

SEPIA - A brown ink or pigment. A photograph in a brown tint.

SHAGREEN - The rough hide of a shark or ray. Untanned leather with a granular surface that is often dyed green.

SIDEROGRAPHY - The art of engraving on steel.

SOCIOLOGY - The study of society.

SOLANDER BOX - A box designed to hold manuscripts, maps, books, etc. Named after Dr. Daniel Solander (1736 – 1782).

SPELTER - Zinc based metal, often called 'poor man's bronze'. Normally thinner and tinnier than bronze but of similar appearance.

STANHOPE - Novelty item with a tiny lens that reveals a photograph when held to light.

STIPPLE - Decoration consisting of tiny dots in an overall pattern.

STONEWARE - Glazed pottery in which both body and glaze are fused together.

SUCROLOGY - The collecting of sugar packets.

TAT - Tasteless, not worthy of serious collecting (by most people), tatty and generally of little value.

TAXIDERMY - The art of stuffing and mounting the skins of animals to give life-like appearances.

TEEKIN - American term for 'antiquing' (buying, browsing, selling).

TEGESTOLOGY - The collecting of beer mats.

TEST PRESSING - The first factory pressings of the record. For circulation to reviewers. Often plain white labels.

TOBACCIANA - Smoking related collectable items.

TREEN - Small wooden objects. Not of joined construction, therefore furniture items not included.

TUNBRIDGEWARE - Decoratively inlaid woodwork, characteristic of Tunbridge, Kent 18th and 19th century. Often fashioned as a mosaic of varying coloured woods.

TURNERY - The art of turning in a lathe.

TYPOGRAPHY - The art of printing or using type.

UK QUADS - Film posters. Generally unique to the UK because they are landscape instead of portrait.

VECTURIST - Transport token collector.

VELOLOGY - The collecting of Vehicle Excise Licences (tax discs).

VENEER - A thin layer of wood used to surface or decorate a piece of furniture.

VEXILLOLOGY - The study of and collecting of flags and bunting.

VICTORIANA - Objects of the period of Queen Victoria's reign (1837 – 1901).

VITREOUS - Glass-like. Usually refers to a porcelain or stoneware fired body.

VITRICS - Glassware and the study of.

XYLOGRAPHY - The art of engraving on wood.

XYLOLOGY - The study of wood.